This Book belongs to
Linda Gordona.
8-1-94.

PARAMEDICS

PARAMEDICS

Paul Chapman

&

Jeremy Mills

BBC BOOKS

This book is published to accompany the
television series entitled *Paramedics*
which was first broadcast in 1994
Published by BBC Books,
a division of BBC Enterprises Limited,
Woodlands, 80 Wood Lane
London W12 0TT

First Published 1994
© Jeremy Mills & Paul Chapman 1994
The moral rights of the authors have been asserted
ISBN 0 563 37081 5

Designed by Grahame Dudley Associates
Photographs by David Secombe
Typeset in Oldstyle by Goodfellow & Egan Ltd, Cambridge
Printed and bound in Great Britain by Clays Ltd, St Ives plc
Jacket printed by Belmont Press Ltd, Northampton

PREVIOUS PAGE: *Paul Chapman in the ambulance cab.*

CONTENTS

ACKNOWLEDGEMENTS

THE BOOK AND the television series could not have existed without the willing co-operation of all the staff of the Northumbria Ambulance Service, in particular the crews at the Central ambulance station and in the Control room. The staff of the hospitals in Newcastle also did their utmost to facilitate the project.

The book owes a debt to Max Arthur for his work on the original material along with Vanessa Daubney and Carolyn Mallam. Sheila Ableman once again provided inspiration and motivation. Margaret Enefer researched and co-produced the television series with tireless enthusiasm; Richard Ranken and Mike Riley filmed the events with consummate professionalism; Richard Cox, Mel Morpeth, Carole Woof, Sally Evans, Warren Harrison, Valentina Giambanco and Ian Freer worked hard on the post production of the films, while Paul Hamann gave support and encouragement throughout.

Above all I would like to thank the patients who co-operated so generously to make the series and the book possible. Where it's been necessary to protect privacy, some names and identifiable details have been changed.

JEREMY MILLS
February 1994

INTRODUCTION

THIS BOOK IS a record of four days in January on paramedic duty at the Central ambulance station in Newcastle, the busiest in the northern region. We cover the city centre and many of the outlying districts so the stories reflect a wide mix of cases.

I've been in the Northumbria Ambulance Service for eight years which have been a time of great changes, not the least of which was the introduction of paramedics. I've drawn on those eight years in an attempt to paint a broader picture of our jobs. Some of the stories reflect the farcical situations we find ourselves in, but most are heart-rending and sometimes gruesome or disturbing. But I haven't pulled any punches. Sanitizing the reality would do a disservice to the patients and my colleagues, any one of whom could have written a similar account.

It's widely recognized that the care given to a patient within the first 'golden hour' after any incident is essential. The skills and techniques which paramedics can put to use in these situations are increasing by the year. I hope that when you've read this account you'll have at least some idea of what our work entails and how, in the future, the paramedic will become increasingly important in the front line of our country's health care.

PAUL CHAPMAN
February 1994

— DAY —
ONE

07:05 AM

THE EMERGENCY 'PHONE in the duty room rang and we were the first of three crews due out. It was the start of four twelve-hour shifts at Newcastle's Central ambulance station. I'd been at the station for half an hour, checking the ambulance over, making sure all the drugs were in place and finding out what dramas the night shift had been involved in. I was on with Karen, another paramedic, who I'd never worked with before.

The emergency call was passed to us as a 'collapsed female' at a block of flats in a run-down area of Newcastle. The term 'collapse' can apply to anything – from someone who feels slightly dizzy to someone who's had a heart attack and stopped breathing. We set off through the first of the day's busy traffic, sirens blaring and blue lights flashing.

When we pulled up at the main entrance to the flats we found that the intercom system had been vandalized and the door was locked. We'd reached the scene within five minutes, but were now stuck outside! There was nobody around, so we banged and banged, but still no one came. Karen got on the radio to Control and was asking them to telephone the caller back just as a chap got out of the lift and opened the door for us. We took the lift up to the tenth floor and were met by a friend of the lady, a man in his sixties. As he led us in through the hallway, which was grey with damp, he told us she'd fallen down and banged her head on the corner of the door.

The flat was really run down. The once white walls were yellow with smoke stains and the place stank of urine. The woman was slumped in a chair on the far side of the sitting room in this poky, dark flat, and we could barely make her out as the only light in the room came through the open kitchen door. Our shoes stuck to the carpet as we walked across the room to her. I asked the chap for more illumination and from somewhere in the gloom he found a table lamp. When he switched it on we saw a pretty grim sight. The woman was covered from head to foot in blood, with more still spurting from a cut blood vessel in her head. A little blood goes a long way. We applied a sterile pressure pad and then bandaged it quite tight, to keep the pressure on. But this didn't stop the blood coming through, so we applied two more pads before it stopped. As we did this, we talked to her in an attempt to discover more history and whether she was suffering from anything else. The first question in our minds when someone falls is *why* did they fall? There are many possibilities, all of which lead to different treatment. Did they trip on the carpet, were they pushed, or did they have a blackout? An important part of our job is to be able to give the hospital staff as much of a background picture as possible in order to help their diagnosis.

We weren't getting much sense out of the woman. The reason was pretty obvious. There were empty bottles scattered around amongst the piles of newspapers and discarded clothes, and she reeked of alcohol. When a patient is incapable of telling the hospital staff anything herself, our gathering of information from the scene can yield vital clues. We stripped off her blood-soaked clothes, which also stank of urine. It was a nasty sight as well as smell. Karen rubbed her down with a towel and found a clean nightdress. Throughout this, her friend didn't stop giving her severe verbal abuse, so there was no love lost there. She needed help, but *he* wasn't going to give her any.

As we were tidying her up, I looked around the place and

couldn't help wondering what had led to her being in this state: there were dirty plates everywhere, drawers open, clothes lying on the floor, faded prints of flamenco dancing girls on the walls and a mouldy, stuffed donkey. It was desperate.

Having got her into a nightdress, we took her to hospital. When we left her the hospital staff were stitching the wound and said they'd wait until she'd sobered up to try and reason with her. But people who end up in her state aren't usually interested in any logical discussion. I've no doubt that once she'd been patched up she'd have legged it.

The conditions under which some people exist never cease to amaze me. Not more than a month ago we were sent on an emergency call to another lady who'd collapsed in her house. The roads were quite busy, but there weren't many men in flat caps driving in the middle of the road so we weaved our way through without much problem. The call was to another rather run-down area of Newcastle and there were hardly any parked cars as we drove along the street. In fact there were more shopping trolleys parked in the gutter than cars, and even they'd had their wheels nicked. So a big gleaming BMW further down the road, outside what we correctly assumed was our house, stood out. When people dial 999 for us they often ring for their GP as well and I assumed this flash car belonged to the doctor.

We were met by a man at the door who said the lady was in the flat upstairs. First we had to negotiate the hallway which was full of junk: a bike, a set of battered old golf clubs and cardboard boxes were piled up high. We had to step over some and squeeze round the rest. The place hadn't been decorated in years and where you could see it the original white paint had become dark yellow. Everywhere there was a musty, fusty smell. As we made our way into the room, I asked the doctor what was wrong with the patient. He seemed surprised. 'I'm not a doctor, I'm her son.'

It was about 9.30 in the morning and bright outside yet the curtains were shut and the room was lit by nothing more than a 40-watt bulb. Sitting on a settee was the pathetic figure of a frail, little old lady. She was surrounded by piles

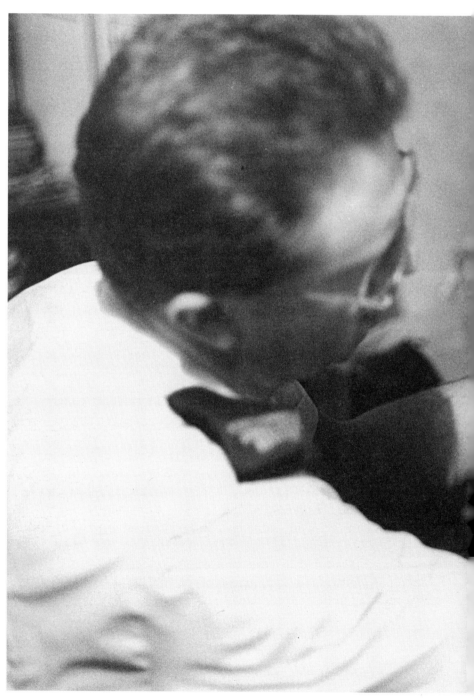

Today's first patient.

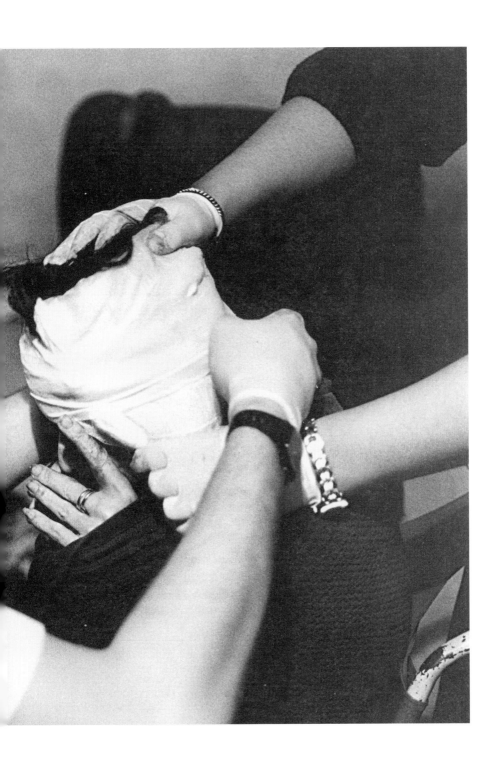

and piles of boxes. They'd taken over the room. They were piled to the ceiling, box somehow balancing precariously on box. Elsewhere in the room were small heaps of clothes. Some had been folded, others left crumpled where they'd fallen. There was just no space anywhere. I asked her son if she was talking.

'Oh yes, she's talking. She just can't cope any more, can't manage the toilet.'

He then said the doctor had been earlier and said she was suffering from malnutrition.

I made my way over to the settee and crouched along-side her, not feeling the urge to sit down.

'What have you had to eat today?'

She said, 'Spam.'

'What about yesterday?'

'Spam.'

'What else do you eat?'

'I only eat Spam.'

Despite the appalling conditions I thought I was going to crack up. It was straight out of *Monty Python*.

'What do you eat?' Spam, spam, spam and more spam.

I asked her son how long she'd lived alone. The reply took some believing.

'She doesn't live alone. I live with her.'

I looked at her clothes. They had been bought in better days and were far too large for her now. They had worn so thin, they were rotting away and falling off her.

I explained to the old lady that there wasn't much I could do for her where she was and we would have to take her to hospital. She was as light as a feather when we lifed her onto our chair. Somehow we managed to get her round the boxes and across the piles of clothes and out into the ambulance. I asked the son if he would like to accompany his mum.

'Oh no', he said, 'I'll follow you in my car.'

I said 'Is that *your* car outside?'

He looked pleased at my interest. 'Oh yeah, do you like it? I've just bought it, fantastic. Fifteen thousand pounds.'

What could I say? There he was living with his mother

in all that squalor and yet he had a brand new car.

All the way to the hospital I reassured her she'd be fine, but sat in dread that she'd mention spam. I know I'd have broken down in tears trying not to break out into the *Monty Python* song. When we handed her over to the nurse in the casualty department all I could bring myself to say was that she'd been living on tinned meat. I hope they persuaded her to try something new to build up her strength.

These strange lifestyles are in no way peculiar to the city. I used to work at Hexham which is to the west of Newcastle in rural Northumberland. One afternoon we got an emergency call to a man who'd collapsed in a forest. The details we were given by Control were sketchy. They didn't know the exact location, or the man's name, but we were to head for a cottage in the Kielder Forest where we would receive further information. On the way I went through the possibilities – a chain saw accident, sports injury or a forestry worker with angina? We turned off the road and, as instructed, went down a track until, as we'd been told, we were flagged down by a lady outside a cottage. She told us to head on down the track for about half a mile, take the next left, and then the next right and we'd be met by some forestry workers. Sure enough, they were waiting for us by the side of the track.

They told us we'd have to do the rest on foot. We left the ambulance on the track and they took us down into the woods in single file along a narrow, muddy path. The further we went the less light there was as the trees became denser and the track became muddier. I knew my mate and I were thinking about the same thing, the ambulanceman's favourite hopeful question: 'Can you walk?' If he couldn't, we'd have an interesting return journey.

While we went along we got some background about our patient from the forestry workers. He was an elderly Pole who'd escaped from a prisoner-of-war camp and made his way to England to fight with the British. As long as the

OVERLEAF: *Arriving at the Freeman Hospital.*

forestry workers had known him he'd live like a hermit in a caravan deep in the wood. His only contact with the world was when they called in with food and other supplies.

At first it was difficult to recognize the green mound ahead of us as a caravan. It must have been there for years. It didn't have any wheels and was covered in moss, so it was well camouflaged. If it hadn't been pointed out we wouldn't have seen it until we were right on top of it.

To get inside the caravan you had to go through a really narrow, low door then swivel your whole body to one side and duck your head. There was no light in there and despite the summer warmth outside it was dingy, damp and cold. There were newspapers everywhere – on the floor, on the table, some folded, others spread out. The whole place was in a mess. The old boy must have liked his tipple because there were a few whisky bottles scattered around, some were standing up with dregs in them and others were on their sides empty.

The old boy was at the far end, lying on what would have been the floor, had it not been covered with general mess. How he existed I just don't know, but that was his palace, his world. The ceiling was very low so I had to crouch down to get to him. Even though it was summertime he had layers and layers of clothing on. And on top of every-thing he had a big brown coat. It was so old and worn that it had a shiny wax finish on it. Then there was the smell. A pungent mixture which still makes me queasy when I think about it.

It was obvious that this old boy hadn't been looking after himself properly for a long time. I asked him his name to see whether he could hear me. He could barely speak and when he did it was in very broken English. As we talked I checked him over. He had a weak pulse and had obvious dif-ficulty breathing. We propped him up and covered him in a blanket. There wasn't much we could do in the confines of the caravan. We knew we'd have to get him to hospital. There was no point in asking if he could walk, it didn't look as though he'd moved for days. I decided that we would have to carry him on our chair. We could never have carried him on a stretcher through the woods, they were so dense. I told him what we were intending to do and tried to reassure him. All the time, at the back of my mind was the thought that he'd probably not left his caravan in years and certainly would never return.

We started to carry him towards the ambulance, accompanied by the forestry workers. I was at the bottom end of the chair, with my mate at the top. We were only about twenty yards from the ambulance, but making slow progress in and out of the ruts made by the large forestry machinery, when his condition grew worse. I didn't like the look of what was happening at all and shouted, 'Come on, let's run for it.' Four of us took a corner each and, as fast as we could, ran through all the mud and clay. When we got him to the ambulance all five of us were covered in dirt.

We laid him down, checked him over and found that he was nearly in respiratory arrest. He'd take a rapid breath, then nothing, another breath, then nothing. He was fading fast. If we didn't do anything the inevitable consequence would be cardiac arrest. As we set off for the hospital, I started Intermittent Positive Pressure Ventilation (IPPV) by

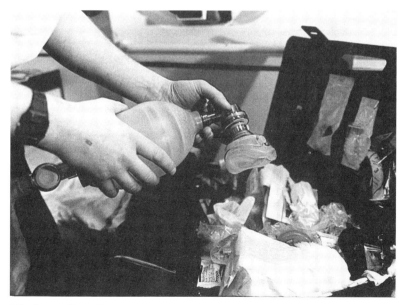

The bag and mask.

ventilating air into his lungs with the bag and mask. It's a basic piece of equipment which has a silicone rubber bag about the size of a rugby ball with a ninety-degree, elbow-shaped tube attached at one end. On the other end of this tube is a face mask which fits over the patient's nose and mouth and makes a seal. Then, when you squeeze the bag, you force air through the mask into the patient's lungs. It's exactly the same principal as mouth-to-mouth resusciation, except that our bag is more controllable. This seemed to help his condition. Every so often he'd breathe on his own. Then another bout of apnoea, when he'd stop breathing and I had to ventilate him again.

Not far from the hospital he deteriorated again and suddenly went into total respiratory arrest. His breathing stopped, but he still had a pulse and his heart was still beating on the reserves of oxygen in his system. I began ventilating him, breathing for him completely with the bag and mask. After a while, to my surprise, he started to breathe again, though very weakly. I gave him as much oxygen as his system could absorb.

When we arrived at Hexham General the resuscitation staff were standing by. We relayed all the information we had about the man. The resuscitation team took over the ventilation, and we helped the nursing staff. The first job was to remove his clothes. In the disinfected surroundings of the casualty department the smell released was incredible. The worst came when we started to remove his boots, or to be more accurate peeled them off. They may well have been on his feet since the War, I'm sure they were of a type that hadn't been manufactured for decades. Even after the strips of what was once leather had gone, we couldn't remove what had, presumably, been his socks. A nurse got a hold from the top and tried to roll them down, inside out, over his feet. But they wouldn't come off. As we probed around we discovered why. Over some considerable time the socks had worked their way between his toes and the flesh had grown around the material so that socks and flesh had fused. His feet were basically rotting away. It was quite horrendous. I remember in the resuscitation room we had the doors open, the air conditioning on at full blast and even then the smell was appalling. His feet were putrefied and had become gangrenous. This explained his respiratory problems, which occur in acute cases of gangrene. We'd arrived just in time.

He survived the experience and went on to have surgery to amputate one of his legs. I would have liked to find out more of his life story but, as so often in these cases, I never saw the old boy again.

07:55 AM

AS SOON AS we finished with this morning's first case we radioed in to Control to let them know we were available for other calls. They gave us an urgent job. Our calls on the accident and emergency side of the ambulance service are divided into two categories. The most obvious calls are emergencies which usually come from a member of the public dialling 999, or sometimes via a doctor. The second category consists of urgent cases which can either be a transfer from one hospital to another or, most often, a call from a doctor asking us to transport a patient into hospital. The doctor will specify a time limit of anything from half an hour upwards to pick up the patient, and unless we find a need when we arrive, we don't use the blue lights. This urgent case was passed to us as a woman who'd been 'off her legs'. It's a phrase which is used all the time, we get about as many calls for this as we do for collapses, with just as many variations.

When we arrived, the house was a complete contrast to the morning's first call. It was neat, well decorated, had decent furniture and certainly no smell of urine. We were met at the door by the patient's sister, a sprightly eighty-year-old. The sister very politely said 'Come on in, she's upstairs, all ready. I'm just finishing her hair.' This is where Karen's talents for hairdressing, more than her paramedic skills, were handy, because she went upstairs and helped the lady. A major part of our job is more to do with reassurance and tender loving care than trauma medicine. You learn from your first days on the non-emergency patient transport service, the part of the service which provides transport to outpatient clinics, that reassurance can often be a more potent medicine than the most powerful drugs.

Only when Karen felt the lady was ready did she give me a call. When I went up our patient had her best frock and coat on and her hair looked very neat. We put her in our chair, wrapped her up in two blankets and took her down to the ambulance. On the way to the Freeman Hospital she explained that she and her sister had lived in the house all their lives, but that they had watched the area slowly but surely getting worse. A few months ago they had been broken into and as a result they'd spent a fortune on an alarm system. I thought to myself that it wouldn't do any good, because people round there might hear it ringing, but they certainly wouldn't come to their assistance. The sisters were beginning to feel safe in their home again when, two weeks ago, they'd woken up to find a bloke in their bedroom, who threatened to kill them if they didn't hand over their money. They were terrified. It was a horrible shock to the system. No wonder she was 'off her legs' and had now decided that she couldn't cope with living at home any longer. It's so sad to see a bright old lady like that, who isn't technically ill, forced to give up fighting. When we took her out into the ambulance we all knew it might be the last time she'd be leaving that house. It was a terrible indictment of our society. Karen and I were both appalled at what we'd heard, but I have long since ceased to be surprised at what one human can do to another.

It's always poignant when everyone present knows that the patient we're taking is leaving for the last time. When it's clear they have all their mental faculties about them it's real lump-in-the-throat time.

We were once given the transfer of a little old lady who knew she was growing weaker by the day and would eventually have to go into hospital. That time had arrived. Her doctor had come out to see her, spoken to the family and told them that she didn't have long to live. It was decided she should leave the big farmhouse where she lived with her husband and their family of five or six, and go to the local hospital. As we arrived it was clear that the farm was well run and in good condition. The entrance to the house was no more than five feet high, very low but very wide. The family had gathered in the kitchen and were obviously upset. We went upstairs and met the lady. She had long, white, flowing hair, which matched her nightdress. She was frail, but still talking lucidly and somehow maintaining a real dignity. We put the lady onto our chair, wrapped her up in blankets to keep her warm and took her downstairs.

As we reached the bottom of the stairs she asked if she could just look into the front room. We wheeled her in and she looked around at all the old familiar objects and quietly mumbled 'thanks'. Then came the hardest bit. I've done it on numerous occasions, I just don't like it, it hurts me. We pushed her through to the kitchen where the family were waiting to say their goodbyes. Her husband was sitting by the table wearing his best coat, his flat cap, white shirt and tie, looking very lost. I wheeled her across to him and he kissed her farewell. She'd probably been born in that house, now she was leaving it for the last time. It's a horrible situation to be in. Any ambulance man or woman will know how you have to cope with your own feelings and those of the family. All we could say to the family was, 'Look, don't worry, we'll look after her for you, and make sure she's nice and comfortable down at the hospital. We'll remind her that you'll be coming down later to see her.'

Once we were on board the ambulance there was little we could do but hold her hand as she watched the farm get smaller through the back windows. It was quite heartbreaking.

08:35 AM

WE'D JUST DROPPED our patient at the Freeman Hospital when the radio bleeped with another job. We were passed the sixty-first emergency call received by Control that morning. It was to a man 'fitting' at a block of flats in the east end of Newcastle. As we pulled up, we were met by the landlord who explained that he'd come to inspect a couple of flats that morning. When he couldn't get access to one of them, he'd looked through the letter box into the hallway and seen his tenant lying on the floor having a fit.

By the time we walked in the lad wasn't fitting anymore, he was maintaining his airway and he could open his eyes spontaneously, but was still very drowsy. I talked calmly to him and asked him what his name was and what had happened. Slowly he said 'Yeah, my name's Michael. I'm not sure what's happened.' We lifted him onto our stretcher, which is really a bed on wheels, and then put him in the ambulance where we gave him oxygen and a lot of reassurance. He began to recover and told us he'd had epilepsy since childhood. We handed him over at the hospital and gave them as much information as possible which wasn't really that much. As we were leaving he suddenly remembered that he'd left his keys in his flat and was locked out. He was still quite groggy but asked if we could telephone his girlfriend to get her to bring his spare flat keys over to the hospital. We passed the request on to the reception staff who were telephoning her as we left. Later we heard that the hospital staff hadn't been able to get hold of her so, very helpfully, decided to telephone the police and ask them to call round at the girl's address. The policeman who was given the job was very happy to oblige since he recognized the girl's name as someone who was wanted for several serious crimes, but who had gone to ground. He turned up at the flat, sure enough, there was the girl and she was nicked. Then, to make the police's day, they checked on the lad's name and he too was wanted for some less serious crimes. He got a lift from the hospital straight to jail, without passing go.

Last month we received an emergency call from the police to tell us that a man was 'fitting' down on the quayside, outside the Law Courts in Newcastle. We get quite a few calls to the Law Courts and you never know whether it's going to be a witness or a defendant still handcuffed to a police officer! We arrived on the scene in a couple of minutes and were flagged down by a policeman on the quayside. This patient didn't appear to have anything to do with any case, he just happened to be passing the courts.

The policeman told us how he'd seen a man walking along who'd suddenly fallen and started shaking. When we got to him he was lying no more than two feet from the edge of the river. I was concerned that he shouldn't have another fit and jerk himself into the water. We managed to move him away from the danger and on to a path. At the time it was raining and he was covered in mud from having thrashed around in a puddle. I wanted to establish who he was, so I checked through his pockets but he had nothing except a spoon. People do have the most weird things in their pockets. Normally those who suffer from epilepsy carry some indication which tells you what medication they are on, and who to contact in any emergency. This chap had nothing.

Some epileptics have no fixed abode and probably no fixed routine, so they forget to take their medicine and that gives us a lot of problems. Many may have been shunned by their family and are unable to hold down a regular job and are not allowed to drive. The world of the person who is not controlling their epilepsy, is a world that is spiralling downwards.

I can understand why people are unsettled when they see someone having a fit, it can be a terrifying sight, especially if you've never seen one before. But they often look worse than they actually are. There's not much you can do for patients having a fit except protect them from doing any damage to themselves as they thrash about. Often the only option is to move any objects which could injure them as their arms and legs are thrown about and just let them shake. It's an old wives' tale about epileptics swallowing their tongue, but it can fall back and block the airway. You should never try to open their jaw by putting your hand inside their mouth. From personal experience they can give one hell of a bite. We insert a bite block to protect their airway.

If someone is in *status epilepticus*, that is a prolonged convulsion, a paramedic can give a drug called Diazepam, a central nervous system relaxant. But we can't give it to anyone who is taking antidepressants or alcohol, because their

On duty with Karen near the Tyne bridge.

nervous system is already depressed. The other problem we have in giving Diazepam to an adult is that it has to be given rectally, so getting someone's pants down in a busy shopping mall and stuffing a suppository up their backside is not the most sought-after job.

As he started to come out of his fit, the man opened his eyes, but he didn't respond to my questions. I was aware that he could start to fit again so I gave him plenty of tender loving care. I wanted to calm him down because anyone coming out of a fit is in a state of 'aura', unaware of where they are or what has happened, and completely out of it. So I talked very gently to him and told him there was nothing to worry about. I checked him over to make sure he had no other injuries and, having got him into the ambulance, we took his clothes off, dried him down with a blanket, covered him in another and put the heaters on to warm him up. I also gave him some oxygen which seemed to help him. We heard later that he'd refused to be seen by a doctor, left the hospital and within half an hour had had another fit and had to be brought in again by ambulance. I was rather pleased it wasn't us.

We were once called to a restaurant where the chef had 'fitted', which he hadn't done for a couple of years. He had told his employers of his condition when he'd been for the job interview and they were particularly understanding. In the office they had a sheet compiled with his photograph, his next of kin, what medication he was on and the date of his last fit. So when he did collapse, the owner knew who to contact and, of course, the information was really useful to us. It also proved how, even with epilepsy, it is possible to carry on a normal life.

09:20 AM

WE WERE TOLD to return to base. There are some days where you can spend the whole shift moving straight from one job to the next, and never return to the station at all, so any opportunity to get back is welcome. When more than one crew is on station we take calls in rotation, so there's always a keen calculation of how many other ambulances are parked up when you drive back in. More than two and you stand a good chance of getting a coffee. If you're the only one you know there's little point in even putting the kettle on. The kettle in our duty room is a very sophisticated piece of technology. When it's switched on it sends a signal to our Control room so that they know to telephone through an emergency call as soon as it's boiled.

When the automatic door lifted we drove in to see that we were the third crew in line. We knew we'd have a bit of time on our hands, so we cleaned the outside of the ambulance. The first two ambulance crews were called out to an accident and we were about to start on the inside when the insistent ring of the red telephone, the hot line to Control, shattered the peace. It was our turn again.

09:40 AM

WE ARRIVED AT a house in Longbenton and were met outside the door by the patient's sister-in-law. She explained that the patient had severe learning difficulties. She'd had a bad turn two days previously and the doctor suggested she be left in bed to rest. But even though she was weak, she insisted on getting up. She had tried to climb the stairs unaided, fallen backwards and cracked her head. When we came to look at her she was very frightened and anxious, and it was extremely difficult to communicate with her. She had a small cut so all we could do, as we bandaged her, was smile and be as gentle as possible. With anyone who's had a fall it's standard practice for us to put their head and neck into a cervical collar. We're always over cautious in any case involving possible neck injuries because there's always a possibility that damage has occurred to the spinal cord and this may be aggravated if the patient moves their neck too violently. Our job is to immobilize their neck and get them to hospital where the experts can examine and, if necessary, x-ray the injury. I explained to the patient and her sister-in-law what we were going to do, but as we tried to put the collar on she began crying and screaming. This was one of those 'what can you do?' situations. Do you have a happy patient without a collar, or an extremely distressed patient with one, thrashing around and possibly doing herself more damage? We decided on the happy patient. From the way she was moving around it was very unlikely she had damaged anything, but we didn't really have any choice. In the ambulance we rolled up two blankets and placed one on either side of her head, to act like a pillow support for her. All the way to the hospital we were talking to her, calming her down. When we arrived, I waited with her in the ambulance, while Karen went in to explain the situation to the hospital staff. It would have been no good if we'd just wheeled her in to a large casualty department with all the chaos, noise and drunks, because she would have been hysterical. Fortunately the nurse was able to find a quiet room away from the main casualty area.

Whenever we get an emergency call to someone with severe learning difficulties it's always a problem. We turn up with no background history of the severity of the condition and have to make instant judgements about the treatment of someone who, often, is unable to communicate with us. I'll always remember the call we had to a fire in an old miner's cottage. When we arrived there were plenty of people milling around, and one of them took us straight to the patients, explaining as she went what had happened. When the fire had started, neighbours had rushed in and pulled out the people who lived there, a mother and daughter. The mother was quite an elderly lady who looked after her severely mentally and physically handicapped daughter. The daughter had no way of moving around by herself, she could hardly move her arms or legs, so her mother did everything for her. We were the second ambulance on the scene and by the time we arrived the mother had stopped breathing. She was black from the smoke and effectively dead. The other crew were attempting to resuscitate her. Our job was to look after the daughter. I shall never forget the look in her eyes. She was terrified, not physically hurt in any way, just absolutely terrified and bewildered by the chaos. People were running past her into her house to try and rescue some of the belongings but her eyes were only on her mother. She could see the crew pushing down hard on her mother's chest and she was scared. Not only must it have been awful to see someone being treated like that, but I'm sure she knew that her one contact with life, her mother, was dying. It was an unimaginable double blow. We moved her a little way away talking all the time and trying to reassure her. But there was no getting away from the fact that as soon as the doctor certified the mother dead and the resuscitation attempts stopped her life was destroyed. And the only way she could express any of her feelings was through those terrified eyes.

It's the nature of this job that you take on board some bloody awful sights and inevitably we counterbalance that with black humour. Like the story of the fireman at a house fire who rescued the old lady. As she thanked him, she asked about her dog.

'Oh, I'm sorry. Your black poodle didn't make it.'

'Black poodle,' she said, 'it was a Golden Retriever!'

10:17 AM

WE RADIOED CONTROL with the details of the last job and were asked to 'wait one'. All of us have this image of Control searching through the computer screens, looking for work when they say that to us! Sure enough they asked us to stand by for details of an emergency call. It was to a man who'd collapsed with chest pains. Another one of those calls which could mean anything. The call was some way off, a journey of at least eight minutes.

During the course of the day we might have five or six collapses, which can vary from somebody who's not breathing, to someone whose legs have turned to rubber because he's drunk. The last serious call I attended which was described in this way was a few weeks ago just after we'd delivered one of our regular night-time drunks to the Royal Victoria Infirmary (RVI) casualty department. We received the call as a woman who'd collapsed with chest pains at a nearby social club.

We arrived within a couple of minutes at around 11.00 p.m. and went to the front entrance, but there was nobody to meet us, which is quite normal. I knew the reception was up three flights of stairs, so we locked the ambulance and took our basic resuscitation equipment and our carrying chair with us. Nine out of ten calls to a social club at that time of night turn out to be that the person is drunk.

When we got to the top of the stairs I asked the receptionist if anyone had phoned for an ambulance. She said, 'I'm not sure. Someone was on the telephone. They might have been phoning for an ambulance. Why don't you try either along to the right – there's a party there. Or the left, there's a party in there too.' We wasted time by going to the right where there were certainly quite a few inebriated people, but no one had collapsed. As we came back to the reception area a chap told us the call was for a woman upstairs. When we got to the room there was loud music playing and people still dancing, eating and drinking. We could see a woman lying on the floor at the far end of the hall. In order to get to her we tripped over the odd bag which people were dancing around and had to say 'Excuse me' to an awful lot of people who had very glazed eyes. When we finally reached the woman, she was lying on her back, which is about the worst position she could have been in. She had vomited up food and we presumed that she must have then choked on it, because she wasn't breathing. There were people standing around or stepping over her and a couple of people shaking her to try and bring her round, but no one had cleared her airway. As we started to examine her we got the usual trickle of information about what had happened. They explained that the party was a wedding reception and this was the bride's mother. She'd been dancing, felt a pain in her chest, had sat down, then slumped forward and ended up lying on the floor.

The first action was to clear her airway. Having put on my rubber gloves, I 'log rolled' the lady onto her side, opened her mouth and swept out the inside of her mouth with my fingers, clearing as much of the vomit out as I could, then aspirated out the rest with our suction equipment. The woman still wasn't breathing. So, having cleared her airway, the next priority was to breathe for her. For this I used the bag and mask. After two inflations I checked for signs of a pulse. There was nothing. The important actions at this stage were to keep pumping oxygen into her lungs and therefore into her blood, and then get that blood pumping into her brain. After only three minutes without oxygen the brain can be damaged, so these moments are crucial.

The heart is a muscular pump and when it stops we have to mimic its action by performing chest compressions, CPR (cardio-pulmonary resuscitation). To do this we link the fingers of both hands, put the heel of one hand near the bottom of the breastbone directly above the heart and then press down onto the chest with straightened arms. The heart is a hollow organ with four chambers. When we squeeze the heart, we force blood out and around the body. Then as we take the pressure off, the heart is refilled with blood.

Since the music was still blasting away, I was hoping the rhythm was right. A good fast track is best because the compressions should be at a rate of around seventy to eighty a minute. If it's a slow, soppy number you tend to be a bit too slow on the chest compression. When we're breathing for a patient and compressing the chest, we work in a particular sequence. I was doing fifteen chest compressions to two inflations. If we'd both been working on her with one bagging and the other doing compressions we'd have carried out five compressions to one inflation. At that moment though, my mate Chris was organizing the guests to help him bring in the rest of the equipment. After I'd completed four cycles of CPR I felt for her pulse, but there still wasn't one.

We carry a combined portable defibrillator and heart monitor on the ambulance which measures the electrical activity of the heart. This is the shock equipment you see so often put to use on the television in dramas, and often incorrectly. The one where the doctor in her nice white coat

OVERLEAF: *A resuscitation exercise.*

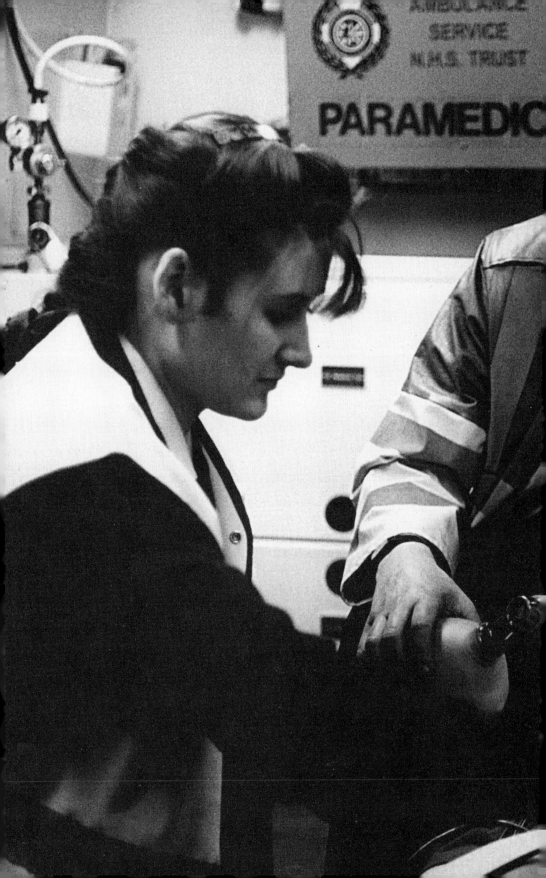

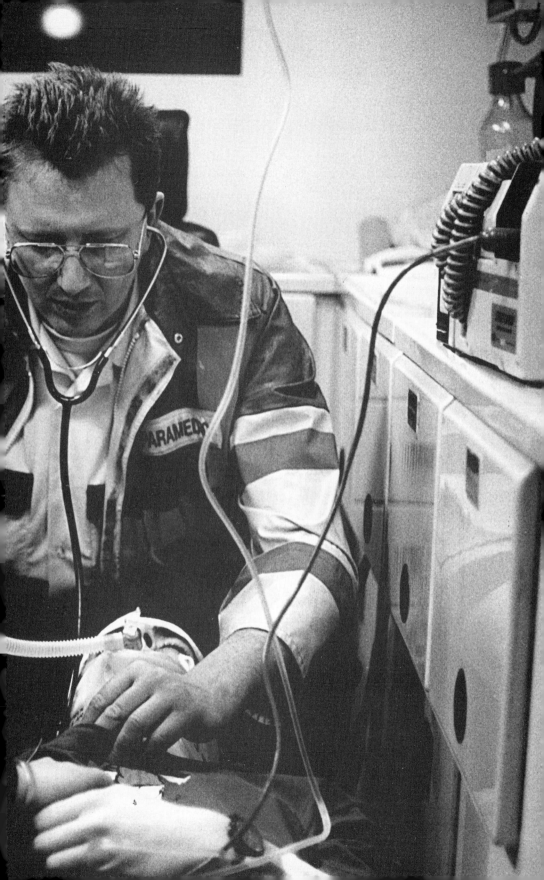

in the clean light operating room pulls the two stainless steel paddles out of the machine, shouts, 'clear!' and gives a shock to the patient who promptly gets up and walks away. I'm sure the common impression is that the defibrillator shock is used to start the heart, in fact they're used to stop all the haphazard electrical activity of the heart. For example, when you hear of someone having a heart attack, they get a pain in their chest and the heart may very well stop beating. But when it stops beating and goes into ventricular fibrillation (VF), it may continue to fibrillate (wobble like a jelly) for some time afterwards as the result of random electrical signals. This is when we can use the shock. When the heart stops altogether, we have a different protocol to follow and drugs to give the patient, but we can't use the defibrillator.

As soon as Chris arrived back with the defibrillator and the paramedic case which carries our drugs, he took over the CPR and I prepared the equipment. By now the guests had realized the mother was in a very bad way. They had stopped the music, put the lights on and cleared everybody out of the room apart from the immediate family. I wanted to ascertain what was going on with the heart. The defibrillator we use, has a small screen which displays a graph of the electrical signals being picked up from the heart via two paddles placed on the patient's chest. I looked at the screen and saw that her heart was in VF. This meant I could give her the shock treatment and hopefully the heart would start. I placed the paddles onto the lady, one on her sternum and the other on her apex, charged up the machine and ordered everyone to stand clear. I held the paddles as firm as I could then delivered the shock by pressing the buttons on each paddle. As I fired the charge, all her muscles contracted. When I checked the screen, the shock had made no difference at all. I had set the machine to give her a shock of 200 joules, which is one hell of a whack of energy. I now reset it at 360, the maximum power our machine will deliver. I then gave her another shock, but she stayed in VF. Then another shock. Still nothing.

We have procedures, called protocols, which we follow in all paramedic situations. In this case we could try three shocks then we have to intubate the patient, that is put an endotracheal (ET) tube, down her throat into the windpipe to maintain the airway. Chris continued with CPR while I prepared the equipment. There is quite a skill in putting the ET tube down the windpipe, since we have to carry this out with the patient on their back and the tongue invariably falls over the airway. We then have to lift the tongue out of the way and at the same time look for the vocal cords. We use an instrument called a laryngoscope to view the back of the mouth. It's a bit like a shoehorn with a light on the end. If you can't see the vocal cords you can't intubate, because the danger is that the tube will be placed down the oesophagus, not the trachea and we end up pumping air into the stomach not the lungs.

The lady was still not breathing and had no pulse, but to intubate you have to stop CPR. Which meant I had to get that tube down her windpipe as quickly as possible. I hold my breath as a guide to a sensible amount of time to allow for intubation. The ET tube is about twenty-three centimetres long and on the end which goes down the trachea is a cuff that we inflate, sealing off the windpipe. Once this is secure, should the person vomit, it can't go down into the lungs and create problems. The other end of the tube connects to our bag and makes the process of pumping the lungs much simpler. If you can't see the vocal cords you have to withdraw the equipment and start ventilating the patient again with the bag and mask. Thank God, I managed to intubate this lady first time. The next thing was to give her a drug down the tube. The drug we use for someone who is in VF after having three shocks and intubating is called Lignocaine. This is a local anaesthetic used to stabilize the heart muscle. Using a syringe, I gave her 200 mg down the ET tube. I then reconnected the bag and mask and hyperventilated her with quick inflations of the bag which got the drug down into her lungs. Then I charged the defibrillator up, gave her another 360-joules shock and lo and behold she wasn't in VF anymore. The monitor showed she actually had a rhythm. I'd restarted her heart! The feeling when you do this is unbelievable. All the weeks of training, the hard slog

Checking the laryngoscope.

of pulling drunks out of the gutter, becomes worthwhile. We had done something positive. When we walked in she was blue, she wasn't breathing, effectively that woman was dead. We'd started to breathe for her and by giving her electrical shocks, CPR and a drug we'd got her heart to beat. It was fantastic.

Her heart was now beating, but very, very slowly at about twenty beats a minute, whereas it should have been pumping away at about seventy-two beats a minute. Even though her heart was functioning she hadn't started breathing, we were still doing that for her. We needed to speed up that heart rate for which we can use a drug called Atropine. But her body was so shut down from shock that all her veins had constricted, so much so that I couldn't get a needle in. I couldn't even see a vein, so I pumped the drug down the ET tube. I saw on the monitor that her heart was speeding up and heading for eighty. I put my fingers on her neck and felt for the carotid pulse – it was strong. She was now stabilizing. We were still breathing for her, but stopped to see if she'd manage it on her own. She could. Her lungs started to work. She was coming back very quickly now. Then she started to regain her reflexes and began to gag on the ET tube. That is perfectly understandable. It's like waking up and finding someone has put a hosepipe down your throat. I took the tube out of her windpipe but still kept doing IPPV with the bag. This assisted the lady's breathing in time with her own.

The next thing we had to think about was how to get her out to the ambulance and off to hospital. We decided to use the service lift. Chris went down and reversed the ambulance as close as he could to the lift. One of the family helped him carry the stretcher while I continued IPPV and monitored her progress. We lifted her onto the stretcher and off we went. Of course when we got her into the ambulance about fifteen people wanted to go with her, even the bride and groom which would certainly have been an unusual form of wedding transport.

We radioed ahead to the RVI so that when we arrived at casualty all the emergency staff were waiting. Even on the short journey, I could see the lady was improving all the

time and breathing spontaneously, but still deeply unconscious. Having brought the person back it was still on my
mind that she might have suffered brain damage, because we
had no way of knowing exactly how long she'd been without
oxygen.

When we handed her over to the hospital team I gave
them as much information as possible about her history and
what I'd done to resuscitate her. They transferred her from
my monitor to their own and she was then their patient. It's
an amazing feeling when you pull somebody back like that,
but there was no time to bask in the glory. As soon as we'd
cleared up we were off to another job.

Within the hour we were back at the RVI with another
of our regulars. We were wheeling in the drunk who was giving everyone the verbals when we heard someone shout,
'There they are!' My first thought was that we were in for it
from someone we'd upset somewhere at sometime. But the
story of what we'd done at the wedding reception had obviously spread among the lady's family. Twenty or thirty of
them were standing outside casualty having a party and
singing away. 'Well done lads, she's getting better,' they
said. And every time we returned to the RVI that night one
of them would see us and come across to give us the latest.
It seemed that she was up in the coronary care unit, and becoming stronger, but the question of brain damage still
remained. The effect of using CPR in cases like this really
makes me think that everyone should be taught the basics of
it. A lot of it is common sense. It needn't take much more
than an hour to learn. Not long to spend on something
which could save a life. Let's be honest, it's a wonderful feeling to know you have saved a life. It's surprising how many
people collapse due to an electrocution or a drowning and
yet, when we arrive, nobody is performing CPR. We get
there as fast as we can, but that can never be straight away.
So if someone is there doing CPR during those precious two
or three minutes after the person has collapsed, the victim
has a far greater chance of survival.

The following day, just as we were about to start our
shift, I rang the RVI and was told that the lady had regained

consciousness and, if we wanted to, we could visit her. Chris and I asked Control if we could have a five-minute break to see the lady. I must admit we were a bit nervous about visiting her, after all we were complete strangers. In the coronary unit the staff nurse explained to her who we were and what we had done. Although she was still weak, she was so grateful and thanked us for saving her life. What brought things home to us was that on her bedside table were pictures of her grandchildren and the rest of her family.

Five weeks later I got a letter from her, again expressing her thanks, and saying that we had prevented the wedding day from becoming a tragedy for the family. I didn't read the letter until I got home after a particularly unsatisfactory day. It made everything seem worthwhile. For once I didn't beef to Claire that night. She knew what resuscitating that lady meant to me. It was just the sort of case most of us join the ambulance service for in the first place.

After I left school I had worked as a swimming pool attendant in Newcastle for five years during which I pulled a few people out of the water. The first bloke in particular sank like a brick, in fact I don't think a brick would have sunk as quickly as he did. I think he just panicked, blew all his air out, stopped swimming and sank straight to the bottom. Up to then I'd only carried out simulations, where you rescue your mates, but suddenly this was real life and the man was literally fighting for his life. I don't know how I did it, but I got him up to the surface and I didn't have to phone 999 because he came to pretty quickly. I suppose I must have pulled out about half a dozen sinkers while I was there, but I never had to resuscitate any of them.

I was quite enjoying the job. I was twenty-four, single and living at home. I had a car and no money problems. I hadn't seen any bad accidents, never seen anyone killed or even dead. Life was good, but there must have been something missing. Then one day a young lad jumped in to what he thought was the twelve-foot end of the pool and found it was only three. He cut his head quite badly, so we called the ambulance which arrived very quickly. I recognized the driver, Ernie Mitchenson, as a regular swimmer at the pool. I'd never known he was an ambulance man. From the day of that accident, every time Ernie came down we'd talk about his job and I got more and more enthusiastic. Some months later Ernie phoned and told me that there were some vacancies.

We underwent a day of tests including maths, English and most importantly, as I have come to realize, being able to point out the quickest route to a location on the *A–Z*. Then we had a manual dexterity test in which we had to take apart a piece of equipment. Ernie reckoned they'd ask me to dismantle a set of Entonox equipment used to administer a pain-relieving analgesic gas. He showed me how this was done and, sure enough, that's what they gave me. The gods seemed to be on my side. I was then given a driving test and passed that all right. The next person to take the test was not so lucky, the gear stick came off in his hand. He was so upset, he was sure he'd be failed, he even offered to pay for the damage! But he got through.

Then there was the final interview. I went into the room which was no more than ten feet long with four senior ambulance officers sitting at the table. As I walked towards them, the room became a corridor. I seemed to be walking for ever and ever. When I eventually sat down I went straight into four-wheel drive motor-mouth. In fact they had to interrupt me to tell me that they'd 'let me know'. I was not confident.

I was on tenterhooks at the baths, jumping every time the 'phone went. I told one or two people that I had applied, so when one of them answered the 'phone and told me it was from the ambulance service I didn't believe them, I thought they were having me on. I had been accepted, pending a medical. The doctor in Newcastle made me touch my toes, cough and see if I could read small print. Then he said, 'Yes, you've passed.' And that was it. After five years at the pool, I was an ambulance man. I finished at the pool on the Sunday and started to train for the Patient Transport Service (PTS) on the Monday.

I've never had to use my swimming skills since I've worked in the ambulance service, although I have been called out to two drownings, both in the River Tyne. The first time some chaps from a factory down on the riverbank were on their break and having a smoke outside when they saw this bloke jump into the river from the opposite bank. One of them 'phoned 999, while the rest ran over the bridge to try and fish him out. When they got to the other side he hadn't come to the surface. Then one of them spotted him and somehow they dragged him out. By the time we arrived they'd flagged down one of the patient transport ambulances taking outpatients to a clinic, and the two PTS ambulance men were starting to resuscitate him. They carried on helping us but unfortunately after all our best efforts he died.

My second drowning was sometime later. When we found the place on the riverbank we saw a young lad being comforted. He was shivering with cold and shock. He and his mate had gone out for a bit of fun and it had ended in tragedy. They'd been larking around and his mate had jumped in and been swept away. He'd dived in to try and save him, but he'd almost become a victim himself. An old local turned up and told us that where the lad had jumped there was a strong current which must have pulled him under, he wouldn't have stood a chance. Later we heard that the underwater frogmen recovered his body.

My first two weeks as an ambulance man were spent on the introductory course where we learnt basic first aid and were told how the ambulance service worked. We then did a week of advanced driving, followed by four days of supervision by a senior ambulance man at Throckley. He familiarized me with the local hospitals and introduced me to a lot of my future patients. I was then let loose as a single-manned PTS driver taking walking cases to outpatients clinics, patients for renal dialysis and old people to day units. We'd pull up at their door, help them on with their coat, make sure they'd got their appointment cards and lock their door. It was really a good training because I had to think about other people, and I hadn't spent a lot of time doing that before.

One Friday, early on in my career, I picked up about eight outpatients from the Freeman Hospital and dropped them off one by one. It was quite late by the time I'd finished and I was looking forward to a night out with my mates. On my way back to the station I heard this clunking in the back. When I looked it was a false leg. But I couldn't remember any of the patients I'd delivered who only had one leg. I had no alternative but to go back round to everybody. So I found myself, with a false leg under my arm, knocking on all these doors asking if they had left their leg behind. Or even worse in my naiveté, 'Excuse me madam, is your husband legless?' Understandably people thought I was taking the mick. Inevitably I found its owner at the last house. All he said was 'Thanks, lad, that's my spare.' He'd been in for a fitting that morning.

During the first year in the ambulance game I used to take an old lady to an outpatients clinic two or three times a week. When I first picked her up she was a sprightly, smart lady but as the months went by I could see how she slowly deteriorated. Eventually the inevitable call came from her doctor to ask us to take the lady into hospital. She was going in for long term care. When I first picked her up I'd knock on her door and she'd show me into the front room while she put her hat and coat on. As time went on she started to meet me at the front door and wouldn't let me in. This time it took two of us to carry her out. When I went into the house the difference was incredible. The smell hit you first. Then I saw that what had been her neat and tidy front room had become her bedroom. It was an amazing sight. There were cats everywhere. Fifteen to twenty of them all purring and meowing. There was no sign of a litter tray and the place stank. She had two double beds in the room and all her beautiful Victorian furniture was piled up randomly around them. Chairs stood on top of a table; a chest of drawers was perched on top of a bedside cabinet. There she was waiting for us, with her scarf and hat on, sitting amongst all these cats. She had let herself go completely. It was just so sad.

You soon got to know the signs that something was wrong when you pulled up at a house. The curtains were drawn, the milk bottles and papers still outside. So you'd look through the letter box, shout, then put your ear to the letter box and hear moans and groans. You'd then shout to reassure them that you were going to get help and radio for an accident and emergency ambulance and the police. Often the neighbours had a key, so you could ask them to let you in. It was a great way to learn how to keep calm and cope. It also made me keen to learn how to deal with similar situations myself, so I applied for the accident and emergency course to learn more advanced ambulance aid.

After a year working on PTS, I was sent on a six-week accident and emergency course which, at that time, was run in Glasgow. I enjoyed every minute of it. Most of it was in the classroom with mocked-up accidents. We worked on people who had been realistically made up to look as if they had been in some horrific accidents. All this was in conjunction with lessons on anatomy and physiology, along with instruction in the rules and regulations governing the conduct of ambulance technicians.

In those days we were issued with a dark blue uniform, similar in colour to the police, and a tie and a cap. Rule number one was, no matter what was happening you had to keep your tie and your cap on. You could be crawling through a filthy tunnel, or dealing with a birth in the most confined space, but you had to keep that cap on. The only difference between the uniform of the trainee and the experienced, grey haired ambulance man, was the fact that their caps had a yellow cover. My sole aim in life was to get one of those yellow covers. As soon as I was halfway through the accident and emergency course I started making telephone calls about where I could get one. I didn't want to arrive at my first accident wearing a shiny cap.

It was an intense six weeks, where we were taught the three Ps: preserve life, prolong life and prevent deterioration. When I left there I was keen to get on the road and put my experience on models into reality. Most of the lads were sent to busy stations. Instead, I was sent to Hexham, a quiet station which had just the occasional burst of activity. It was mostly rural work, with long journey times, but it was a good training and built up my confidence in handling casualties.

After five years on A & E I passed the paramedic entrance exam. Having learnt about basic ambulance aid the appeal of being a paramedic was, and is, the ability to help your patients with advanced skills.

Ambulance care has come a long way in twenty years. Then you turned up, did basic first aid, bundled the casualty on a stretcher and went off with the bell ringing. Most of the ambulance services were run by the local council, so you could be on the dustcart one week and the next you'd be on the ambulance. These days every A & E ambulance person has been on a six-week course, so they are far better equipped than a first aider. The paramedic has undergone intensive training on top of that. We can administer drugs and carry out advanced resuscitation techniques which give the patients we deal with a better chance of survival.

Most hospital staff now recognize our skills and the usefulness of the background information we give them when we hand over patients. Increasingly, we've become involved in working with the nursing staff to continue treating patients once they're in casualty. This has helped to build up a high level of respect between most doctors, nurses and paramedics. Paramedics are not doctors, we don't go to medical school, we don't go through those years of clinical training, but we are a vital front-line force and we have a high level of skill in the immediate care of A & E patients. When you work with an experienced doctor, who takes notice of your information, questioning you about the patient's history, it's a great feeling. Especially days later, when you see them on another case, and they come across to say, 'We saved that old lady you brought in last week. That really makes it all worthwhile. It's all part of the motivation to do the job.

There are some occasions when we arrive at a call and know it's a lost cause. But our rules require us to attempt resuscitation in all cases except where there's extensive post mortem staining, or rigor mortis has set in, or there's obvious decapitation. There's a continual debate about whether this is right or not, and whether we should have more discretion over which patients we should leave alone.

Recently I had to escort a patient with terminal cancer. It was a long way from the hospital to her home so her relatives had been warned that she might not survive the journey. There was nothing more the hospital could do for her; she had hours to live but wanted, if possible, to die at home. Had she remained in hospital they would have let her slip away with dignity. They would not have attempted resuscitation. But our protocol is different. If she'd stopped breathing while we were attending her we would have had to attempt resuscitation. We may not want to, we might think that common sense should prevail, but our rules say that we resuscitate, until a doctor certifies death. There are obvious reasons for this. The main one being that we're not qualified to judge what the long term prognosis is for any patient. More importantly, by attempting resuscitation even when we know it's pointless, we're seen by the relatives to be doing something. You can hear them saying years ahead, 'Oh, we had two paramedics out to her. They did everything to save her, but she didn't make it. At least we tried.' The point is that through us carrying out our procedures, the family feel *they've* done all that they could.

Fortunately, in that lady's case we got her home. I would dread to think what state her family would have been in had we arrived outside her house and they'd found us zapping her chest and thrusting tubes down her throat. But I wonder whether the time will come when we're allowed to use our professional judgement on whether to resuscitate or not depending on the prevailing circumstances. I hope it does.

As we raced off this morning, Karen and I discussed the thought that we recognized the name and the address of our collapsee. As we got closer, it clicked. I began describing him to Karen, 'Rotund, rugged man.'

Karen said 'Oh yes, I've brought him in before, he always leans over the garden gate.'

'That's him,' I said, 'and his daughter has big fluffy slippers.' Sure enough, as we went over the brow of the hill there he was leaning over the gate with his daughter in her big fluffy slippers.

Our sixty-a-day man.

I didn't need to ask his history because I knew already that he smoked sixty cigarettes a day. He'd had chest pains on and off for years and had been told by every doctor in Newcastle to stop smoking. He was on medication, but he frequently forgot to take it. Of course you couldn't lecture him, he'd had all that, I wouldn't do it in any case. I wouldn't want someone telling me to stop drinking for instance, especially while I was doing it!

In the ambulance I gave him oxygen. For once, he'd remembered to take his Salbutamol. This is the same drug paramedics can administer, so there was nothing more I could give him. When we got him to hospital one of the staff told me he'd been brought in only three days earlier, had been told to cut down on his smoking and to remember to take his medication!

People's attitudes to calling an ambulance run the gamut from those who see it as a free taxi service to those who are reluctant to 'bother us' even when they are very ill. None of us minds getting a genuine call, even if it's obvious when we arrive that there's no real urgency and the patient's condition didn't really warrant a 999 call. I always feel that if anybody is unsure, they should 'phone us.

Every day we get emergency calls to cases described variously as lacerations or a collapse. We hare off through the city centre risking our lives to get there as quickly as is safely possible. When we turn up we find a fit young lad who, sure enough, has cut his finger, but it's not even bleeding. Or a person who felt a bit dizzy because they stood up too quickly. Those cases are frustrating when you know there are people who are really ill out there, but at least we've been called with genuine intent. What we do get annoyed about are the thoughtless time wasters.

Last month we had the perfect example of being regarded as no more than a taxi. We were at Blaydon when our Control came on and asked us to attend an assault case. They warned us that an ambulance had been to the scene earlier, but had been turned away because the injured person didn't want it. When we arrived at the house we were met by a lad who didn't appear to have any obvious signs of having been assaulted. I asked him what had happened and he said, 'Me mate threw a loudspeaker at me, and it caught me on the forehead and it's hurting a bit.' When I looked carefully I could see a small mark, hardly even a bruise. I asked him if an ambulance had called earlier.

'Oh yes,' he said, 'One called, but me other friend hadn't arrived and I wanted to wait for him to come to hospital with me.'

I told him that he was right to call the ambulance if he was hurt, but his injury really didn't look serious. He said 'Well I think it is, and me friend's here now, so you can take us.'

We are not allowed to refuse, so we gritted our teeth and put them both in the back of the ambulance. They were pushing their luck when they asked if they could go to the General Hospital, but we delighted in explaining that we had to take them to the nearest casualty at The Queen Elizabeth Hospital. The final comment as we handed them over to the nurse was, 'What time will you be back to take us home?' They were very lucky not to end up with worse injuries than they'd started with I can tell you. I think it's important that we educate the public as to when, and perhaps more importantly, when not to 'phone for an ambulance.

However, I remember one particular job which proved that not all calls to collapses are dramatic in the medical sense. A lady was lying on a bed, which was too springy a base to perform CPR, so we had to move her onto the floor. My mate had put on a bit of weight over the previous weeks and was bulging at the seams. As he bent down to lift the lady he ripped the backside out of his trousers, they were in two halves, split from top to bottom. The only thing keeping them in one piece was his belt. He had the loudest pair of bright red boxer shorts you'd ever come across, from which everything was hanging out. There we were, trying to be serious and trying to save this woman and he was flashing his all at everybody. In the end we saved the lady, but not his dignity. For once it was not only the patient we had to wrap up in a blanket to get out to the ambulance.

OVERLEAF: *Examining the crushed finger.*

11:10 AM

WE WENT STRAIGHT from the hospital to an emergency call to a primary school where a girl had trapped her finger in a door. We had the name of the school and the street, but couldn't find the way in. Eventually, after a bit of a search, a teacher pointed us in the right direction and we found the classroom round the back. A young girl had accidentally jammed her fingers in a door. Her teacher had wrapped a tea towel round her hand, but the poor girl was screaming the place down. We picked her up, talked quietly to her and carried her onto the ambulance. When we took the tea towel off, the injury wasn't bleeding too much but one of her fingers was badly squashed. I put a clean dressing on, but kept it quite loose.

We were just about to drive off, when I saw a lady waving frantically as she ran towards us. Her coat was flapping behind her and you could tell it was the little girl's mother. She was out of breath and could barely speak. The mother was very anxious about her child's finger, but we told her the hospital would treat it with no problems. We also reassured the little girl that the doctors and nurses were really nice people and wouldn't hurt her too much. I don't think it's right to say they are not going to hurt you at all, because when they inevitably do, that child will never trust anyone at a hospital again.

We were then given permission to go back to station for a meal break but, as usual, I'd forgotten my sandwiches, so we made a quick diversion to the pork butcher for a saveloy and peasepudding sandwich. We had the rarity of a full half-hour lunch break. I was just settling down to my third cup of coffee when I heard that inimitable ring.

12:15 PM

ANOTHER EMERGENCY CALL to an old lady who'd collapsed. There were few details except that the police were on the scene. I knew the road in Scotswood, so it didn't take us

Happier after treatment.

long to get there. We spotted the police car outside the house and saw the front door was open. The police had everything under control and had been to fetch the patient's daughter who was now comforting her mother. We discovered that the old lady remembered falling down, but didn't know why she'd fallen or how she'd hurt her leg. When we examined it, we found that she had some nasty lacerations, but it didn't appear to be broken.

She'd been lucky because that day the council had started some work outside her house. One of the chaps had knocked on her door to tell her what they were doing and as he'd not got a response, he'd looked through the letter box, seen her on the floor and called the police. He was a joiner and had managed to get the door open for the police. She'd told them her leg hurt and they'd assumed she meant broken, so dialled 999. We took her to hospital, for further tests to see why she had collapsed.

On another occasion I was filling in at a neighbouring ambulance station last year, when we got a call to go to a block of flats on a huge housing estate. Control told us that there was a lady having a heart attack and in severe pain. As we pulled up outside the flat we were met by a neighbour who was obviously distressed. She said, 'My friend is having a heart attack. I can hear her screaming. I've been knocking away at her door, but she can't hear me. She's stone deaf.' I put my ear to the bedroom window and I could hear screams of agony. She was obviously in great pain. A policeman arrived and we quickly told him the score. As he was about to break the door down, the woman's daughter arrived with the flat keys. She still had her nightdress on beneath a big coat and she wearing a pair of furry slippers. Having heard what had happened to her mother, she was obviously in a state of shock. She turned the key in the lock, the door opened a few inches, but her mother had applied the security chain. The policeman took over. He barged the door once with his shoulder, then again and it shot open. We ran for the bedroom where the woman's shouts and moans were now very loud. I bent over her to start an examination and put my hand on her wrist as I started to talk to her. Her eyes opened and she shot bolt upright. She'd been in a deep sleep having a terrible nightmare. Unfortunately the sight of two ambulance men and a policeman towering over her must have convinced her that her nightmares had been real. She promptly fainted. Fortunately we left with no further misadventure.

We got a call a few days later to go to a collapse. The caller had told control that he had knocked on his neighbour's door and as he'd not answered he had looked through the letter box and seen him lying on the floor. He had continued knocking and shouting but had got no response, so he had dialled 999. We had great difficulty finding the flat because the place was like a maze. The lift was out of order and I remember we had to walk up several flights of concrete steps to the flat where we found the neighbour on his knees calling through the letter box to his mate Charlie. He was relieved to see us. I looked through but all I could see was a pair of legs. A minute later a social worker arrived and explained that as the man was under the care of the Social Services so they had also been called out. I told him the circumstances and he gave us permission to break the door down. Strictly speaking we should have waited for the police, but that man inside needed our help. My mate who is half my weight said he would have a go. He stood back a few paces, made a run at the door and crashed against it. The door didn't move. All he got for his trouble was a badly bruised arm. Fortunately for us a huge policeman, a six-foot monster, arrived. He bashed the door with his foot several times and eventually it burst open. As I started to examine the bloke on the floor he lifted his hand and smiled. He was blind drunk. My mate was more damaged than him. He doesn't try and knock down doors these days.

13:30 PM

WE WERE TOLD to pick up an urgent case, a patient with head injuries, and transfer her from the Freeman Hospital to Newcastle General for a scan. These are the calls which require the skills of ambulance personnel, but for which, despite the term urgent, there's no rush. As we were heading for the hospital, Control came on the radio and said, 'Stand down from that urgent job, we have an emergency call for you.' The emergency calls obviously take priority, no matter what you're doing, even if you're about to start your first meal break after ten hours on duty!

The address was only three streets away from where we were. Once inside the house we found a lady who'd cut her face badly, hurt her jaws and split her lips. There was quite a bit of blood around. She was very pleased to see us, but very apologetic. Two hours earlier she was getting off a bus whilst still talking to a friend and tripped on a broken paving stone. As she had two shopping bags she couldn't put her hands down to save herself and had fallen face down. She didn't want people to fuss and had insisted that she would be all right. But when she had been home a couple of hours and the bleeding inside her mouth hadn't stopped, she'd 'phoned 999. We told her that she had done the right thing, but she did say how guilty she felt about calling us out. We soon ran her to hospital where they patched her up. Later in the day, when we were coming in with another patient, we saw her going off looking much better.

One of the big changes since I joined the ambulance service is the increased awareness of illnesses transmitted through blood, such as hepatitis and in particular AIDS. The possibility of catching it is always in our minds and one of the reasons we're always so careful to wear gloves whenever there's any sort of case which might involve a spillage of blood. Since we go into most of our emergencies with little idea of what we'll encounter, we usually wear them. They also have the advantage of forming a barrier between us and some of the other pretty unpleasant substances we encounter. The business of barrier prevention becomes more complicated when you get to mouth-to-mouth resuscitation. We carry our bag and mask with us but if we were off duty, or on occasions where there are several bodies in need of resuscitation the theory is different to the reality. What I usually do is pull off my t-shirt or use a handkerchief and cover their mouth with that. You simply can't be too careful. The only time I would take a risk without even thinking about it would be where a child was concerned.

14:10 PM

WE WERE CALLED to transfer a patient from a large mental health unit, to one of the casualty departments for an x-ray. The mental health hospital is not a place in which those of us on A & E find ourselves very often. When I first went there years ago on PTS, all the wards were numbered. Then they changed the numbers to names. A few years later, they changed some of those names again. When we got to reception we asked for directions to the ward. The reception-ist said there was no problem, 'Go out of where you are now, turn right, fourth opening on the left and you can't miss it.' So we turned right, took the fourth turn on the left and went into an empty ward. We saw a gentleman cutting the grass and asked him where the ward was. He didn't know where *he* was, let alone the ward! I felt embarrassed, but had to go back to the receptionist and explain that the ward wasn't where she had said it was. She said 'I'm so sorry, it was my fault. I meant to say, go out of here, turn left, and it's the fourth building on the left.'

'Ah, got it,' I said, sure that we were on course now. Off we went, counted the buildings and when we got to the fourth it was unoccupied. We looked upstairs and downstairs but nothing was to be seen. We were beginning to feel like bit players in a *Comedy of Errors*. Back we trudged again to reception and this time there was another woman on duty. We explained that we were growing old and thin looking for this ward. She apologized and said, 'Oh no, they've changed that ward, it's on the other side of the hospital.' She explained how to get to it and told us she would 'phone and make sure a member of staff would be waiting for us. We got into the ambulance and, as directed, came to the opening, turned right and found that the road forked to the right and left. The helpful receptionist hadn't mentioned about a fork in the road. We took the right fork and of course it led to a dead end. Then we saw a male nurse over to the left waving at us. I was getting a bit impatient by now and said to Karen, 'Why don't you just cut across the grass?'

Karen was none too happy about that idea. 'We'll get stuck!'

'You'll not get stuck,' I insisted.

So we cut across the grass. And we got stuck!

After churning up quite a bit of ground, we managed to reverse out. The nurse then led us through a stone archway, down a flight of steps, along a dingy corridor and down more steps until we finally ended up on the ward. Hampton Court maze would have been child's play!

We found another male nurse in charge and from experience asked, 'Is this man violent?' And he said 'No.' The first thing the patient did was take a swing at me and then try to bite Karen.

'Well,' he said, 'he's not *normally* violent.'

We decided that we'd need a stretcher to help restrain him, then I realized that there was no way we could negotiate the stairs or the corners with our stretcher – or even find our way back! Even the nurse said 'Oh, I get lost round here and I've worked here for thirty years.' Then he said 'You go and get the stretcher and I'll wait. Go through the double doors at the end of the ward and you'll see a lift on the righthand side. Go down in the lift, and when you get out go through the doors straight in front of you, turn right, turn left and you'll see a set of doors and go through them.' Off we went. We found the lift, got out and straight in front of us was a brick wall. The only other way out of the lift was to turn left, which we did, and there was a huge sign saying NO WAY OUT.

I said, 'OK, let's go right,' and we ended up in an unused ward. It was completely bizarre, the only thing left was a piano and while Karen was frantically looking for an exit to the outside world, I got on the piano and started singing 'Bring me Sunshine'. I tell you, we didn't know what to do or where to go. We were falling about with laughter. In the end we decided to go back to the door marked NO WAY

OUT. We pushed it open and ended up in another ward.

A rather tough looking nurse said 'Yes, can I help you?'

I replied, 'Yes please. Way Out? Our ambulance is out-side there.'

She said rather brusquely, 'There is no way out through this ward, you'll have to go back the way you came!' We finally got back to the first nurse and told him that we would become inpatients unless he showed us the way out. We followed him and were a bit surprised when he led us to the ward we'd just been sent away from. The formidable nurse was there to greet us again.

'I've just told your friends, you can't go through here.'

Well, the first nurse wasn't taking any of this. 'I have been coming through here for the last thirty years, how else am I going to get out?'

She finally yielded and we reached the outside world. When we had first entered into this nightmare of a place, it was sunny, life was good. Now it was teeming down and we were very, very wet. We brought back the stretcher and I got the chief nurse to coax the man onto it and hold him while we strapped him on. We had been given the job at 14.10 and it was now 15.12! We'd been lost for nearly an hour.

When you consider the number of places we get sent to every day it's not really surprising that we sometimes make mistakes. Not long after I'd started on the accident and emergency service we were given an emergency call to a lady who couldn't stop vomiting at a house with the number eighteen. For once we thought we'd have no problem finding it because when we got to the road, people were standing on the pavement waiting for us. They waved us down and pointed to the house. We pulled over and someone said, 'Quick, he's in here.' I thought, hang on, we were called for a woman, but we went in thinking that the game of Chinese whispers had been played again.

Inside the house there was a chap with a bit of a chest pain, which was nothing serious. I asked if there was a lady ill in the house but they just shrugged their heads. I said to my mate, 'This is strange, I'm sure they said it was for a lady who was being sick.' I persevered. 'You're sure there's no one else in the house who wants an ambulance?' They were definite, 'Oh no, it's Fred here, he gets this chest pain every now and then when he's been overdoing it. He's just taken his tablets for his angina and we thought we'd call an ambulance.' Little old Fred sitting there was fine. It was more of a safety measure that they'd 'phoned us. We took the old chap outside and were about to drive off to the hospital when another ambulance pulled up. I asked what they'd been called for and the driver said, 'To pick up an old chap with chest pains at number twenty.'

I looked at the number on the door through which we'd just brought the chap and sure enough it was number twenty. Our poor vomiting lady was still waiting in number eighteen next door. It must have been a million-to-one chance of two people living next door to each other telephoning for an ambulance at the same time.

Another trap I fall into on a regular basis is making the wrong assumptions about patients' relationships. The other day I was picking up an old boy with heart problems. An attractive young woman fussed about packing a suitcase for the old chap. After getting him onto our stretcher I asked him if he would like his daughter to come with him to the hospital. 'It's not me daughter, it's me bloody wife.' I had to do a rapid, verbal back-peddle on that one!

15:43 PM

WE HAD JUST begun our meal break when the 'phone rang. It was the 'phone call we all dread. A baby had stopped breathing. That was the only information we had. We knew the location and flew there. We found mum standing at the roadside holding her baby while her friend waved us down. I jumped out of the ambulance with my resuscitation gear, and Karen opened the back doors. The adrenaline rush you experience on these calls is amazingly powerful, but you have to remain totally calm.

OPPOSITE: *The baby suffering from apnoea.*

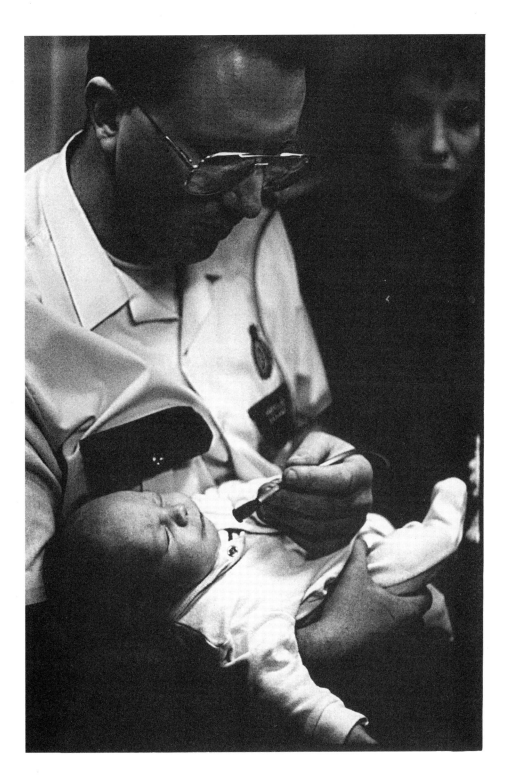

As I ushered the mother into the ambulance I could see that the baby was breathing. It's hard to express the sense of relief. As we sat them down I asked what had happened. The baby had been born prematurely, and been unwell for the past three or four weeks, running a high temperature. Now she was suffering bouts of apnoea.

Understandably the mother had the baby wrapped in two big thick blankets, so the poor kid was piping hot. I calmed the mother down and stripped the baby off down to its vest. I could see she was breathing normally, and the apnoea had probably been caused by simple overheating. Throughout the journey to the hospital I gave the child as much oxygen as possible by holding the maskless tube near her face. By the time we arrived at hospital the baby was breathing normally and we knew she'd be all right. But no matter how many times you receive that particular emergency call, you never get blasé about it.

One Thursday, about a month ago, the emergency 'phone in the duty room at the ambulance station went at 9.30 a.m. In a calm voice the controller, Mo, gave me details of the job. A child had stopped breathing. I was on with Jason that day and he already had the ambulance running by the time I'd taken down all the details. I leapt in, switched on the siren and blue lights and we were off. Neither of us knew the actual road name we'd been given, but we knew the area and headed there in order not to lose any time. I thumbed through the A–Z to pinpoint the location.

We get a large number of calls to children where the only details we receive are that the infant has stopped breathing. In the vast majority of cases the child is having a heat-induced fit and there's no real danger, it's just very distressing for the parents. However, at that time of the morning you fear the worst. It's just the time of the day a mother might go to wake up a child who's apparently slept on for longer than usual, only to discover that there's no sign of life. The adrenaline really pumps on these jobs and you know that all the other crews and everyone back at Control who'd overheard the call coming through would be willing us to get there in time to do something. We all feel the same way about calls to children, they're so helpless, and vulnerable, yet have so much ahead of them. I'm sure it affects me more now that I have my own four-year-old, Christopher. You want to be able to work miracles.

Jason is a pretty speedy driver in normal circumstances but knowing that a child's life could be in the balance guaranteed that he was stopping for nothing. We had quite a distance to travel and were doing well when the inevitable happened. Coming up to a roundabout a real Sunday driver decided he was not going to give way and we nearly bought it. Only Jason's nifty high speed manoeuvring avoided a trip to hospital for all of us. Jason is not one to hold back his feelings and the air was blue with obscenities and vitriol purely through frustration.

I still couldn't find the road on the map. Control were also having no luck looking up the address on the computer. It often happens on these real emergency jobs. Sometimes the family are in such distress that they don't give the correct details when they call in. We've even had people giving their mother's address or a previous house, and the longer our search fails to come up with the correct road name in the area we're travelling to, the more you fear that you might be rushing to completely the wrong address. We'd almost arrived in the district we'd been given but still had no idea exactly where the road was. The prospect of simply having to stop to ask a passer-by, or waiting for someone else to come up with a solution really makes you sweat. You've got to be in that situation to appreciate that everything rests on you, yet Control, who are passing you the job, don't know exactly where the place is and neither do you. It's a nightmare scenario. All the pressure is on.

I tried looking up every spelling combination I could think of but still couldn't find anything. Then the radio bleeped and Control came back to us with the answer. It was a brand new estate off a road we knew well. The sense of relief was almost physical. Knowing exactly where we were heading at last, I concentrated on fitting the air bag with the small face mask we use for resuscitating children, and put it back in the first response case ready for use.

As we turned the corner into the main street we knew the problems were not solved. We found the new estate on the left side of the road, but as we approached we could see the houses were arranged in blocks of about a dozen, and the numbers appeared to have no logical sequence. The only thing to do was to jump out and leg it. I grabbed the first response case and ran along between the blocks looking for the number. We wanted number ten and the closest I could find was fifteen. I ran along the back of this group, saw eleven but then the houses stopped. The next block seemed to start at twenty four. It's impossible to describe the feelings of frustration at moments like that. There was no one around to ask. I ran back the way I'd come and there on the far corner was a woman waving her hands and shouting. I followed her down a path to an open back door. It had only taken six minutes from leaving base to arriving at the scene but felt a hell of a lot longer.

Inside the house there seemed to be a large number of people all in a state of shock. Everything about the situation had bad vibes. As calmly as I could I said, 'Where's the baby?' Someone in the group said, 'Upstairs', in a strange, unhurried way. I took the stairs two at a time, listening as I went hoping to hear something. On the landing I could see from the wallpaper that one room was a nursery, went in and across the room to the cot.

The baby was lying there motionless, like a white porcelain doll. As I leant over her it was obvious she was dead, and had been for some time. When I picked her up I could feel that rigor mortis had set in, and purple patches of post mortem staining had formed where she'd been lying.

What do you do next? Do you go downstairs and say to the parents, 'I'm sorry, but your baby's been dead for some time.' Our guidelines tell us not to attempt to resuscitate anybody with rigor mortis, and if the patient's an elderly person you just have to break the bad news as gently as possible. But with a baby the situation is horrendous for everyone. Even with all the publicity about cot deaths on the television and radio, nothing prepares you for the devastating reality of the situation.

That morning I was aware of the sound of crying from downstairs, and I knew from experience that I had to fight back my own emotional responses. The family downstairs would all be waiting for the paramedic to work a miracle. And despite all the training, the experience of similar cases, and even knowing the reality that the baby was dead, I had to attempt something. I cleared her mouth with my little finger, put my mouth over the baby's nose and mouth and started resuscitating. Two fingers on the chest pumping the heart. It's always the same, something inside says, 'Just keep going, you might be wrong. Keep resuscitating, this could be the one miracle.' What I needed was somebody who was dispassionate to look over my shoulder and say, 'Hey mate, just leave it.'

Jason had brought the ambulance closer to the house, and come upstairs. He only needed to look to know what the situation was. I told him to get the mother and persuade her to come in the ambulance with us. I believe the parents should come with us, come hell or high water. I'm sure it's important to keep the bond going, and to be with the baby until the doctor at the hospital confirms the position.

As Jason organized the family I carried the baby through the house out into the ambulance, resuscitating as I walked. The mother got into the back with the grandmother. I shielded the baby slightly from them, resuscitating as we sped to the hospital. Jason called Control to place the hospital on stand-by to await our arrival. It might seem strange, but even with the sirens blaring and the engine straining, there was a stillness over all of us. The mother had stopped crying and was staring ahead of her, the grandmother just held her daughter's arm, dazed.

When we arrived at the hospital I carried the baby down the corridor towards the resuscitation room where I knew the team was waiting. This was the first moment the family were separated from their child. They were taken into a waiting room while we continued into the resuscitating room. The look I gave the doctor told him that we were too late, but I carried on trying to breathe life into the baby while he examined her. It took a matter of moments for him to confirm death. Little was said. 'You've done your best lads, she's been dead for more than an hour.'

Why do I always have this need to do something in these child cases? Part of me says it's a simple hope that some miracle may happen; another part says that there's a genuine need for the family to feel that everything possible was done to help, however hopeless we know it is. But deep down I suspect that in these, out of all deaths, I don't want to be the person who has to make that final pronouncement. It may be cowardly, but it must be easier for the hospital staff to be relatively dispassionate about it, and I'm not sure I'd trust myself to have to go back to the parents and confirm what they already know. Somehow once you've been in the room, seen the toys propped up in the cot and, however briefly, become part of that awful scene it's just too difficult to be objective.

There aren't many cases that really stick in your mind, but the four cot deaths I've attended will never leave me. They knock you for six, physically and mentally. My knees always shake. I was weak for the rest of that day.

When we got back to the station we felt flat. In our job black humour abounds, it has to, but with cot deaths or the death of any child, no one makes jokes. It brings even very experienced ambulance men to tears. When we walked into the duty room there was an understanding comment or two. They'd all heard the call on the radio as they been on other jobs and knew the score. But you know there's no point in dwelling on it and you also know that Control can't say 'Sorry for what happened, take a ten-minute breather. Have a cup of tea.' It's the one time you're glad when the next call comes in. It's easier to get back out there than dwell on things for too long. Equally I knew that Mo in Control had been in tears as I'd given her the simple log details for the job, it hits everyone. After every cot death, when I get home and see Christopher, I think it could have been him. Then I have a few beers, put my feet up in front of the fire and try and unwind. But there's very little sleep that night.

16:03 PM

WE CONTACTED CONTROL to see if we could get back to the station to finish our meal break. Needless to say, as we were pulling up at the entrance of the station the radio went with another emergency call. A collapse at the Family Planning Clinic. The mind boggled.

It didn't take us long to get there, but as we pulled up outside the heavens opened, it was lashing down. We were met by a concerned woman who told us the man we were looking for was in her office, but explained that he was not a client. The gentleman concerned was one of our regular customers and he was drunk out of his skull as usual. I could only surmise that he had found the nearest doorway, made his way to the office and then refused to budge. Today, though, he tried a new additional justification for a lift to hospital. He told us he had a head injury card on him and needed to go back to casualty. They're pretty canny, some of our regulars.

When a patient with head injuries is discharged from casualty they're given a card which tells them that if they start to suffer from sickness, dizziness or double vision they should report to the hospital. Through the alcoholic haze he kept muttering about this card. Of course it was quite possible that on this occasion he was a genuine case. But when I asked to see the card he made a pretty wild swing at me, so I gathered I was asking the wrong question. It didn't take us long to realize he was just looking for a warm place for the night. He certainly wasn't welcome at this particular inn. I told him I would take him to hospital, but that he'd have to calm down or else I would 'phone for the law. As with most regulars, when he heard the mention of the boys in blue, he came quietly. We took him down to casualty. Whether he got a night's shelter, I don't know.

Every ambulance service has its regular patients. In Newcastle we have about a dozen of them. Sometimes you pick up the same regular three times a day and every day that week. Most of them are very good actors; they can fake unconsciousness or simulate a fit really well. Those who are really accomplished will choose their stage set carefully. They won't choose a dark and dingy alleyway for their performance, they want the limelight. So they usually select a pitch outside a well lit shop window or by the door of a busy fish and chip shop where they can guarantee a large audience. Having chosen their stage they will then begin to shake, fall to the ground and continue shaking. Naturally, before long, someone will call an ambulance. Some ambulance men get very frustrated with regulars. I can understand that very well, but there is no way we are going to cure the problem.

The regular is usually just a very sad attention seeker who knows every trick in the book to get it. Often all they want is a lift to the hospital where they know they'll probably get a hot drink, warmth and shelter for at least an hour or so. When you're called out to them you just speak to them in a firm, but polite voice. With the public around, you can't kick them up the backside and say, 'Look, plonker, stand up,' even though you might feel like doing it, especially if the call comes ten minutes before the end of a twelve-hour shift. In reality they are all down-and-outs, with no home and no hope. We're polite to them and do our best for them but we do get annoyed.

16:30 PM

CONTROL GAVE US permission to return to try for our meal break. We thought third time lucky. In fact we were and managed to have two cups of coffee and twenty-seven minutes of bliss on the recliner chair until our friend the telephone rang.

16:57 PM

KAREN TOOK DOWN details of a road traffic accident at Kenton Road. This is not a good time to drive through Newcastle, but for once, no one was driving in front of us with a flat cap. But it was chock-a-block, with lines of stationary traffic. These are always dangerous situations for us, because on several occasions we've had some impatient motorist who hasn't looked in his mirror or bothered to signal and done a U-turn right in front of us. When we turned onto the Kenton road we must have overtaken a mile of stationary cars without any problems. As we were approaching the roundabout at the end of the road we saw a police traffic car coming down on the other side. He slowed down to tell us that they hadn't found a road accident. We got back in touch with Control who told us to wait while they 'phoned the caller back. It turned out that the call had been made on a car 'phone and that the true address was Kenton Lane, not Road.

Not that long ago, if you were driving along and saw an accident you would stop at the next 'phone box and call the emergency services giving a fairly accurate bearing. Today many people use their mobile 'phones, which is often a blessing in disguise. It means they can report the accident immediately from the car. However, it's quite amazing how many people don't even stop, but just keep driving. They're often strangers to the area and by the time they come to give the details they can be quite some distance from the accident and have no precise location to give. So our controller gets a call about a really bad smash on the Gateshead to Sunderland road! This ties it down to a stretch of road only twenty miles long. It also means that quite often two or more calls come in for the same job, all with descriptions and locations different enough to warrant sending a crew to each, just in case they really are different calls. We seem to waste more and more time these days chasing road accidents which end up miles from where they're reported to have been.

When we arrived at this evening's RTA (road traffic accident) we found a five-car collision. We knew, therefore, that there would be at least five possible casualties, the drivers, who may have suffered whiplash injuries if nothing else.

At any incident involving the possibility of a large number of casualties, whether it's a road accident, plane crash or a large scale fire, we operate a triage system, named from the

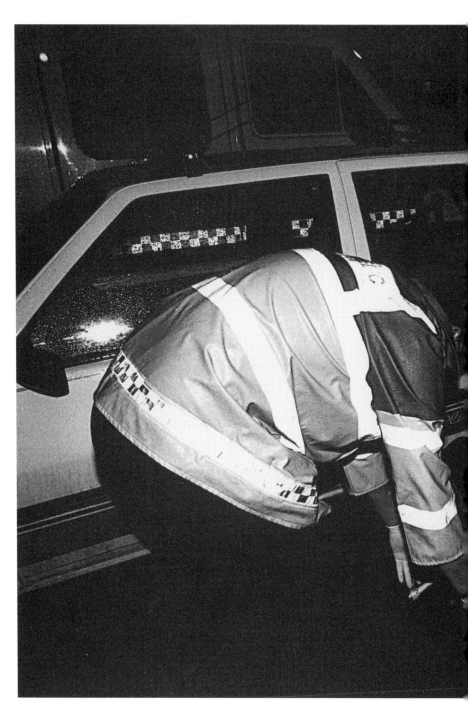

Moving the victim of tonight's road traffic accident.

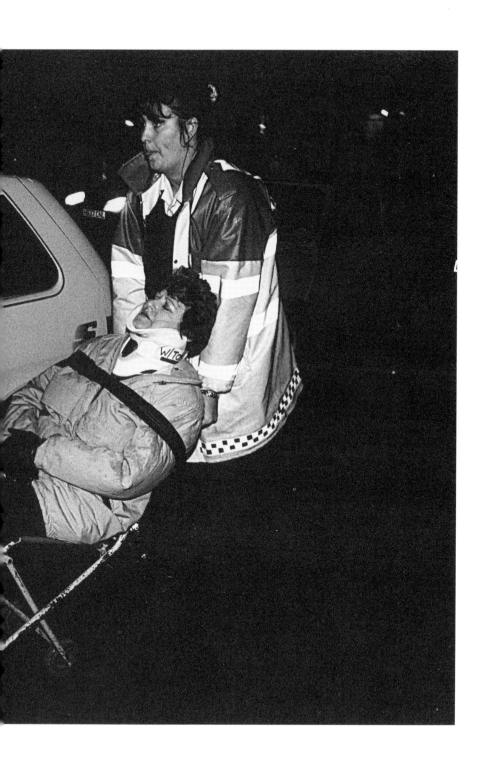

French word meaning sorting. The first ambulance crew on the scene makes a brief examination of every person involved, often simply by walking along, to sort through the casualties and assess the order in which they should be treated. Obviously the seriously injured are first and the bruised last. But somebody critically injured and likely to die, won't be treated until the seriously injured have been seen to. The brutal reality is that there's no point in spending masses of time on a patient who's so badly injured that they are going to die. It's the most difficult part of the job. We're trained to help everyone and not walk past but there are times when you just have to.

In our training exercises for these events the one casualty you can be sure they'll throw into the scenario is a person who screams for help, but is not badly injured. The difficult decision is to be strong enough to carry on past them until you have an overall picture. Every ounce of compassion is tugging you towards helping that screaming person, but you know you've got to carry on until you've assessed everyone, and prioritized them all.

Tonight we split the triage. Karen went to the first two cars and I moved along the others. It was obvious that the leading car had stopped suddenly, and the four cars behind had crashed into the back of it. Fortunately in this particular crash, which had been at low impact, there were only two people injured. The most seriously hurt was sitting in the passenger seat on her own. I asked her where the driver was and she said, 'I am the driver.' Somebody had very foolishly pulled her out of the car, which is the last thing they should have done. There was no danger of the car catching fire or being hit by other traffic, and she was clearly breathing and maintaining her airway, so she should have been left where she was found in case she'd sustained any back injuries. It's the same with pedestrians, leave them where they are unless they are in danger. This lady had been taken out of her seat and then felt faint so had been put back in the passenger seat. I spoke to her to reassure her that she would be all right and that no one else had been hurt in the accident. It is a classic response in a car crash that people, often seriously injured or on their last legs, are very concerned about other people, especially if they feel responsible for the crash.

You sometimes have to become the peace keeper when emotions run high at road accidents. If you arrive before the police you quite often find the two drivers slugging it out or at least shouting abuse and making unkind remarks about each other's driving skills. You learn very soon that it's hard to mediate between two people who've just seen their beloved cars pranged, and who are blaming each other. They don't want anyone interrupting their debate. Some of the people we've picked up after road accidents have definitely sustained more injuries after the crash than from it.

It's quite common at road accidents to have to pick up all the occupants of the cars involved in the crash if they're not too badly injured. The one question you learn never to ask when you're on the way to hospital is the one you'd really like to: What happened? At best you get a stony silence, at worse they start having a go at each other all over again, which is no fun in the back of a swaying ambulance.

Another common but strange reaction you get after an accident is called disassociated behaviour. We had an old lady once who was in a hell of a state, yet all she could talk about was a tin of dog food she'd bought for her pet. On the way to the hospital she kept asking if we'd picked up the tin from the road, not a mention of her injuries.

The driver this evening complained that her neck was hurting so I put a cervical collar on her and we lifted her carefully out of the car, and onto our chair. We then transferred her to a stretcher and I rolled up two blankets and placed one each side of her head, and taped her head to the stretcher to immobilize it further. It was probably a bit overcautious but I think it gave her a sense of reassurance, and it's always better to err that way. Nobody else wanted to go to hospital, so we asked them to sign our book which simply says: 'I decline treatment for personal reasons'. It exonerates us, should someone complain at a future date that they were not treated by an ambulance.

We drove as smoothly as possible to the hospital where the emergency team was waiting and a doctor examined her.

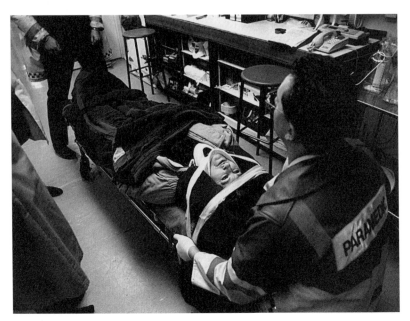

The driver waiting to be assessed in casualty.

She was confident that there was no serious injury and gave us the OK to move the patient from our stretcher onto a hospital trolley. For this we used a special sliding board called a patslide, so that the patient is simply slid across on the stretcher's canvas without having to alter his or her position at all. She thanked us and the last we saw of her was being wheeled off for an x-ray.

18:05 PM

WE'D BEEN BACK on station for a few minutes' break, but were soon off on another emergency call to a collapse at a block of flats in the east end of Newcastle. When you get called to any block of flats, the walking cases are always on the ground floor of a building with two immaculate lifts, while the major trauma cases are on the seventeenth floor of a block where only one shabby, very slow lift works.

OPPOSITE: *Arriving at an emergency call.*

We gained access to the lobby and went up in the lift to the third floor where we were met by a relative. She took us in to the flat where we found an old boy lying in the centre of his living room. He was very pale and his fingertips were what's known as cyanosed, blue in colour. His skin was cold to the touch, but then so was the whole room. It was a freezing day, yet there was no heating in the flat. The old boy appeared to be dead, except that I could see him breathing. He was obviously suffering from hypothermia.

I found out from the relative that his name was Billy, so I got down to his level and said, 'It's OK Billy, you're all right now, we're here and we'll look after you.' While I was saying this I felt for his pulse, which was slow, about forty, and very weak. His pupils were dilated and his breathing was very shallow. He knew where he was, but his level of consciousness had been lowered and his trousers were all wet with urine. We took these off and dried him down with a towel, wrapped him in two blankets, carefully put him in our carrying chair and took him down to the ambulance. I asked the relative to gather all his medication and to make sure his flat was locked.

On the ambulance we kept him wrapped in both blankets, but I decided to use the thermal space blanket as well. This is the silver foil blanket you see marathon runners wrap themselves in at the end of a race. On top of the thermal blanket I put two more blankets. As we got closer to the hospital he began to respond, his pulse rate went up to about sixty and his level of consciousness increased. Recovery from hypothermia can be quick if it's caught soon enough.

We once got a call to a farm where there had been a collapse. Usually in these old farmhouses, the fire's blazing away, there's tea on the go and a really homely atmosphere. But in this case there was no fire and it was deadly cold and very quiet when we walked in. All we could see was a man's feet sticking out from under the kitchen table. We immediately felt his legs and he was cold as clay and stiff as a board. Well dead, I thought.

Of course we needed to make a more comprehensive examination so we crawled under the table to get a closer look at him. I started to move his clothes so that I could feel for a pulse and all of a sudden he opened his eyes. My mate was so shocked he jumped and cracked his head on the table! The old boy was far from dead, but was suffering from hypothermia along with very bad arthritis which made his joints stiff. Once we warmed him up he quickly improved.

In Billy's case tonight I was concerned that the reason for his collapsed state may have been more serious. I had noticed that the lefthand side of his body was weak. I asked him to squeeze my hand and tried to gauge how much control he had of his limbs. We had found him lying on his left side which could have caused the blood to stop flowing to the limbs on that side or it could have been a sign of having had a stroke, which might have triggered his collapse in the first place. As in so many cases it would have been interesting to have stayed with him once we got him to hospital and to have found out what had caused his collapse. The problem is that on a busy station like ours we haven't got the time.

Perhaps it is all part of a clever scheme. If we followed up every case, we'd be emotionally exhausted. As a paramedic you have to learn to shut off, otherwise you'd be overwhelmed by emotion and you'd be no good for the next patient. He or she wants your skills, they don't want your grief or despair. To be truthful Billy was also our last patient tonight and we were glad to get back on station to hand over to the night shift, and leave for home.

— DAY —

TWO

06:30 AM

ANOTHER 6.30 A.M. START. When I looked on our board I was teamed up with Karen again, and the vehicle we'd been allocated had just arrived back from a job. I had a word with the paramedic who'd been using it to find out if we needed anything, but all was intact. We then did our basic checks inside the ambulance before finally looking at the oil, water and fuel. All the training in the world is useless if you run out of petrol on the A69.

When we officially came on duty at 7.00 a.m. there were three crews on duty ahead of us on the rota and for once I was able to sit back on one of the recliner chairs and read the paper. As an extra bonus, the kettle wasn't speaking to the 'phone, so I was able to make several cups of coffee.

08:00 AM

AN UNUSUALLY LATE first call to a diabetic patient who was unwell. We had to weave our way through fairly dense traffic and when we found the road, cars were parked bumper to bumper on either side. This meant we had no option but to park in the middle of the road, blocking it. This particular street is a well known short cut between two main roads and once you're on it you can't turn round. As I jumped down I made straight for the house without looking back, knowing there were about ten cars behind us, containing drivers who were not very happy.

Inside I found a young chap in his early twenties whose wife was a final year medical student. She had no difficulty explaining what had happened and gave us a full history. I checked to see if he was hypoglycaemic, but the blood sugar count indicated that he was normal. If he had been hypoglycaemic, we could have given him an injection of the drug Glucogon or a milk drink with sugar to raise his blood sugar level. We thought it wise to take him in, as he looked a bit weak and it wasn't apparent what was causing this state. I covered him in a blanket and, as we walked outside, I couldn't help notice the huge queue of traffic from both ends. I was glad it wasn't an emergency where a swift exit was required because it took the cars in front of us an age to reverse. I was also pleased that Karen had chosen to do the first six hours of driving!

We were fortunate that this morning's patient was docile. Some people going through a hypo can become very violent. I've had a case in a pub where it took both of us ambulance men plus two large policemen to restrain the patient, which was a lesson in careful diagnosis. When you're called to pubs you have to take care not to jump to the conclusion that all violent people slurring their words are drunk.

09:24 AM

WE WERE PASSED an emergency call to the west end of Newcastle. A patient 'fitting'. A doctor who was on the scene had telephoned and asked if we could attend. It took us over five minutes to get there and when we arrived this old chap was blue and still 'fitting'. He was known to be epileptic and on this occasion he was having a 'grand mal', which means he was 'fitting' continuously. We inserted a plastic tube to

OPPOSITE: *Checking the patient's airway after his fit.*

maintain his airway should he have another fit. While we supported his head the doctor gave him the muscle-relaxing drug, Diazepam, which helped enormously. She then started to telephone around to find him a hospital bed. Meanwhile we learnt more about his history from his mother, who looked after him. When he was about three years old he'd fallen down concrete stairs and banged his head and had been subject to fits periodically ever since. His mother, who was in her nineties, was now finding it too difficult to look after him, so he needed to go into hospital to recover.

The doctor rang around the specialist departments of all the local hospitals looking for a bed, and we waited with the old boy. He was exhausted from his fit and still blue. After some while the doctor returned to the room to say that she'd located a bed in the RVI. We got the man into the ambulance, made him comfortable and laid him down on his side to help maintain his airway. We also gave him oxygen therapy, so by the time we got him to the hospital his colour had come back and he was more or less conscious. He didn't know where he was, but he could open his eyes on command, which was a good sign. The doctor, who had attended him, had written a note about his history and what medication he was on so we handed him over to the ward.

The last time I was called to the same street in the west end of the city was to a bizarre collapse. When we arrived at the scene we thought we'd got the wrong house, or at least the wrong details, because there was a lot of shouting coming from inside. As we went in we could tell that the whole family seemed to have had quite a bit to drink. I asked the usual, 'Did you call for an ambulance?' and the woman in the kitchen just nodded towards the room where the noise was coming from. I'm always reluctant to go into rooms where it appears there's some sort of contest going on. I have no desire to be a hero, but we thought we'd better take a look. In the room two lads were laying into each other on the settee with great energy but not much accuracy, as every other swing seemed to fall wide of its mark. They were still knocking seven bells out of each other though. Beyond them was an old man propped up in an armchair watching the TV.

He was obviously deaf because the set was vibrating with the level of sound coming from it. But old grandad was not too bothered by not being able to hear the TV or by any of what was going on around him because he was very dead.

The first thing I remember saying was, 'Hang on a minute lads, have a bit of respect,' and then, 'Would you mind turning the TV off.' Of course they couldn't hear me so I said in a louder voice, 'Can you turn the TV off.' I said all this and yet they continued fighting. I can't remember who turned it off in the end, I think it was the mother. She knew grandad was dead and she'd been waiting for us to turn up so the show could begin. She also knew what to expect, she'd seen it done, probably on that same rattling television set in the corner.

We got old grandad onto the floor and my mate and I started to resuscitate. Then it was boof, bang, crash, wallop as the two fighting blokes fell on grandad. I wasn't best pleased, but I tried to stay calm. 'Look, keep out me way, I'm trying to see to your grandad here,' but they kept going so I had another go. 'Look, if you don't stop fighting we're going to get the law.' This at least got their attention.

'Oh, well we've been drinking,' as if this would excuse and allow their actions, and then it started again.

I told my mate to radio from the ambulance for the police. This meant I was left alone with these two blokes fighting and two or three others who came to help argue the toss, while I was still trying to resuscitate. The next time I looked up the mother was standing there, leaning up against the door between the kitchen and the sitting room, fag hanging out of her mouth, and a glass of whisky in her hand drinking away. It was not a situation I enjoyed. If they'd turned on me I wouldn't have stood a chance. Then my mate arrived back and shouted at them, 'The law's coming, you'd better stop.'

Even though it was clear we were too late to do anything we tried to get some information out of the woman. What emerged gradually, was that grandad hadn't been feeling too well, so they'd propped him up in his chair to watch the box while they all went down to the pub. The family had come back really really drunk and found him still in the chair but not looking very well at all. She said that they'd known he was dead, but we still got called. Between grandad being found dead and ourselves getting there, a classic fight broke out with one blaming the other, you know, 'Well you left him and you shouldn't have left him', 'I didn't leave him, you left him'.

When the police turned up the fighting stopped, but one of the family ran away. The police were worried in case he came back and attacked us, so we had police protection while we were taking the old boy out to the ambulance. I kept having visions of this bloke jumping out from nowhere and laying into us. What a night that was.

It's often the case that the family provide us with more hassle than the patient. In real emergencies they're all wound up and when things are really bad they want to take it out on someone, and who are the first people to walk through the door? The most common cause for abuse is when the family feel we've taken too long to respond to their call. This is usually unjustified, just that the six or seven minutes between them dialling 999 and us turning up seems like an age. But I can sympathize with the anger, I'm sure if it was one of my family I'd feel the same.

There are national guidelines which lay down the maximum response times to emergency calls. But the simple fact is that there will never be enough ambulances to respond to all cases instantly. If we doubled the number we have, we'd still want double that again, because there will always be a time when they'll all be in use, however infrequent that is. And you can guarantee that very time is the moment you need one vitally for a resuscitation job.

A couple of weeks ago, we were sent on an emergency call to a reported collapse in the street which had apparently been witnessed by a member of the public who, doing their good Samaritan act, had dialled 999. The call was genuine, the patient's illness was not. We arrived just in time to see the police carting off one of our regular drunks to let him spend some time in a cell to dry out. When we radioed in that our collapse had been given a police escort we were immediately given another collapse just around the corner. We got to the housing complex in two minutes but the number was the problem. As we were looking, Control kept asking for our location and for an ETA (estimated time of arrival) which seemed odd as we'd got to the place so quickly.

When we got to the house to say the family were going to kill us was an understatement. Not only did we have the problem of trying to assess the mother but we had to deal with the family, shouting and screaming and threatening to lynch us for taking so long. We thought, bloody hell, it's only taken us a few minutes, what's the problem? Common sense would dictate to them that an ambulance would take more than two minutes, but of course they had been waiting for what must have seemed an age. What we didn't know was the call had been received by Control a few minutes before we had been given the job, but the local ambulances were busy and another ambulance from some distance away had been called in to cover the job. As luck would have it, we were near, but occupied with our regular drunk, which meant that we might as well not have existed. The mother was in a bad way so we had to start a full resuscitation attempt.

These procedures are difficult enough in hospital, where the teams work in an ordered clinical environment with the patient on a nice solid trolley, plenty of people to help, lots of light, back up equipment and space. By contrast we were trying to resuscitate an elderly woman between the bed and the wall, with no space. Yet we had to give her shock treatment and monitor her heart's activity, then get an ET tube into her, and give the right amount of drugs. Her life depended on us.

However, all the time we were attempting resuscitation her family were hurling abuse at us. Before too long we made the decision to cut and run; get her out of the house and off to the hospital. If we'd stayed any longer they'd have had us. We could have called the police, but what good would that have done in this situation? It would only have got them more agitated while we waited for the police to arrive. They were just projecting their anxieties onto us. As it was we got her into the ambulance and worked on her until we got her to hospital. She was lucky, she lived.

Of course I can understand people's attitudes in these situations, it's not a nice thing to see someone being resuscitated, particularly if it's a loved one. I wouldn't like to see it done to any of my family even though I know what it's all about. Tubes going down their throat, electrodes being stuck on, needles being inserted into veins and electric shocks being given. It's not the most pleasant of things to watch, particularly with an elderly patient, where you're giving strong compressions on the chest and you can hear the ribs cracking. So I realize why we often come up against the same problems with families. You're doing your best and they're screaming in your ear, 'Is she breathing? Is she alive? Has she got a pulse?' What do you do? Do you say 'Yes', knowing you're telling a lie, or do you say 'No' and risk being too blunt. All I say in any resuscitation situation is that we're doing our best, doing everything we possibly can, just bear with us.

I get frustrated when people don't let us get on with the job in hand but I know that if the patient was my relative I would want to know that the paramedic was doing everything possible. I'm sure I'd be asking the same questions.

10:15 AM

WE IMMEDIATELY RECEIVED another emergency call to Gateshead, just over the River Tyne, to a patient with abdominal pains. Outside the house we were met by two old boys. I said, 'Where's the patient, what's happening? There's supposed to be someone here with abdominal pain.' When you get calls like this, the adrenaline is running and I wanted to know what was happening.

'Ah, it's me,' one of them said. 'I've had this little niggling pain in my stomach for about four weeks now.'

I asked him if he'd been to his doctor. 'Oh, no, I don't want to bother him, I thought we'd better call you.' Well,

Our 'abdominal pain' case.

ours is not to reason why, so we took him to the local hospital in Gateshead. He walked off the ambulance and into the hospital where we explained to a casualty doctor what his problem was and that was the last we saw of him.

Not wanting to 'bother' the doctor is quite a frequent comment. We got a call one morning to a child with breathing difficulties. Always a highly charged call. We hared off up to the estate in a bit of a notorious area of Newcastle. When we got to the house we went through the door past a kiddie of about eight or nine playing football in the garden. We went straight in and there was the mother, a massive woman. I said to her, 'Ambulance. Child with breathing difficulties?'

'Oh, he's the lad outside; he's had a touch of asthma for the past couple of days. He's got a bit of a wheezy chest.'

The anger just welled up inside me, I couldn't believe it.

I felt like walking up to her and putting my hands around her neck and giving *her* breathing difficulties. I was really cheesed off. The rush through the traffic with all that adrenaline flowing, was for no good reason. When I'd calmed down I asked her why she had called us. She said 'I didn't want to go to the doctor's.' And I said, 'Well, why not?'

'Well, I'd have to go down to the surgery and sit there for ages. I thought it would be easier to 'phone for the ambulance to get us straight to casualty and we'd see the doctor down there more quickly.'

There was a bloody bus stop outside her door, but oh no, our service is quicker and just as important, free.

It's the sort of thing that happens quite a lot and really hacks us off. People who could get buses in or make their own way to hospital, use us as a taxi service. The worst thing is that calls like that take you away from possible real emergencies.

11:05 AM

NEWCASTLE UNIVERSITY CAMPUS is spread over a large area so we do sometimes have problems locating people. At the call this morning, however, the security chaps at the entrance were well organized, and waiting to direct us to the PE centre which we could see from the gates. Inside we were shown to a squash court where we found a lad who had obviously fallen badly and twisted his leg. He was in severe pain. I offered some reassuring words and explained to him that we were going to put a Loxely splint on his leg. The splint is about a leg's length, has three sides which leave the top of the leg visible, and is held on with Velcro straps. We padded it out to make it a bit more comfortable and delivered him, and his mate, to the local hospital which is literally across the road.

I'm not convinced that all this keep fit is very healthy. A few weeks ago we got a call for a collapse. It was a fast, five-minute journey through a lot of traffic. When we got there the old boy who lived in the house was in a panic. It turned out that he lived with his brother who was about seventy and a keep fit fanatic. He had a bit of a gym in a shed at the bottom of the garden. His brother had become anxious when he'd not come out of the gym after his usual half hour. He'd gone to the shed and found his brother lying on the bench press with the bar holding the weights at either end, across his neck. It was one of those contraptions where you lie on your back and lift the weights straight up above your chest and then bend your arms to bring the weights down. Something had gone badly wrong. He was dead, presumably from the injuries caused when his neck was crushed by the bar. We called the police because we weren't certain how it had happened. The inquest pronounced it as an accidental death and put it down to his arms giving way.

11:35 AM

WE HAD TO wait awhile this morning at the hospital while the casualty staff removed our splint and put their own under the squash player's leg. We only carry one of this type of splint on each ambulance so they're jealously guarded.

We radioed in to Control that we were clear, and waited for them to offer the magic words, 'Return to Base and try for a meal break'. We were not in luck. Instead they told us to 'wait one'. So we sat outside casualty waiting for the call, chatting about the finer points of saveloys and pease pudding. Karen expressed her disgust of anything to do with pease pudding, while I staunchly defended it as a delicacy. My taste buds were getting into quite a state when the radio bleeped at us: 'Central 295 we have an emergency call. The police have reported a shooting incident in Jesmond, would you like to make your way and we'll send further details when we get them.'

Quite frankly the answer was no, we did not want to make our way. When we turn up at most calls people are relieved to see us. When there's someone with a gun this is not always the case. Thankfully before we could get any more wound up, Control came back on the radio to tell us

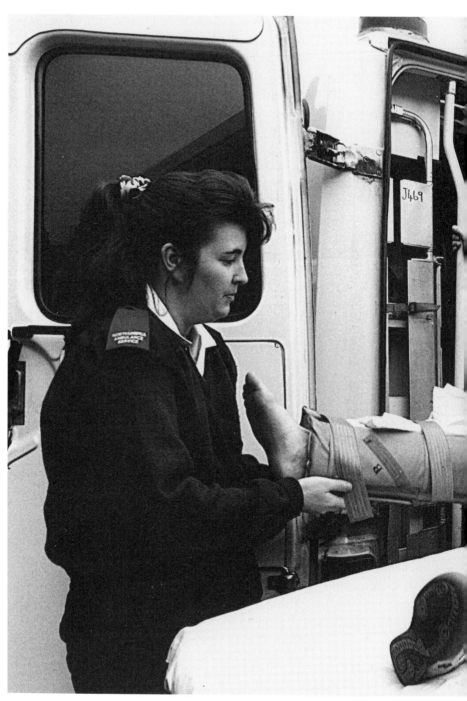

This morning's squash player in the Loxely splint.

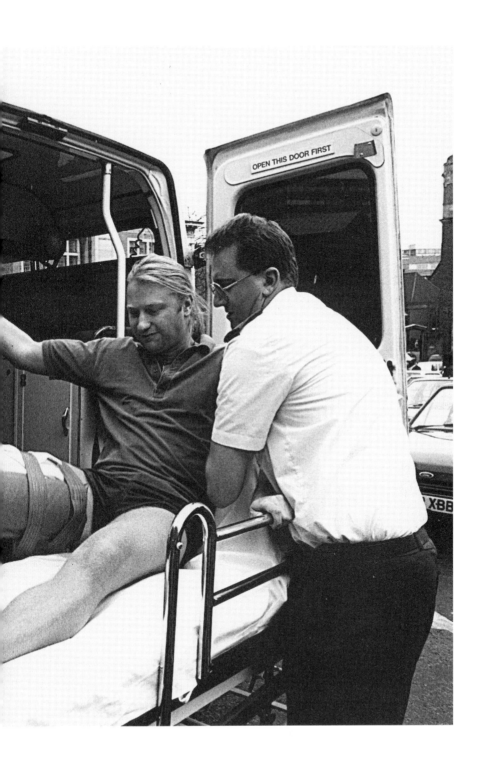

that the police had stood us down. It had turned out to be some kids mucking around with an air rifle, and there were no injuries.

I was at our neighbouring station, Blaydon, last year when we were sent off to a domestic incident a few miles up the valley, without any precise details of the location or job. We quite often get calls from Control to head to such and such an area and they'll let us know the address and more about the incident as we're travelling. I hate those calls because I like to know what I am going to and prepare for it mentally. After all it's a bit different heading for a maternity case than it is for a resuscitation, but off we went.

Control soon came back with the address. We'd been travelling for about five minutes when we got another call from Control. 'We've had a second call. This one says it's a shooting incident.'

When we arrived at the entrance to the cul-de-sac, we didn't see any other blue lights so drove down cautiously. Then a chap came out of one of the houses shouting, 'Quick, there's a man dying over here.'

We went up the path and there was a policewoman crouching alongside a prone figure. The window of the porch had been blasted out and there was glass everywhere, crunching under foot. We said calmly, but firmly, to all the neighbours who had gathered round him, 'Please just give us some room.'

He was lying on his side. We rolled him over slightly and could see he'd got extensive shotgun injuries to his chest and his face. There was nothing we could do for him. His brains and lungs were out. He was dead. It was not a very pleasant sight.

I then asked the policewoman the question that's always on my mind in these instances, 'Where's the bloke with the gun?'

She was clearly very shaken but replied, 'I don't know.'

Now, in all fairness, she'd got the call as a domestic while she'd been on another job with a colleague. They'd been dealing with a car which had been found abandoned, when they'd received the report. They decided she should go ahead while her colleague finished the car job. From what I gathered later it was only as she'd been approaching the house that she'd been given more information, but she was on her own. When she arrived she got the fright of her life and she was in a hell of a state.

However, a neighbour said 'Oh, we've seen the bloke who did this speed off in a car – he's away.'

I can tell you that was a relief. Whenever there are guns around I always think of Hungerford. One person's been shot, have other people been shot? Could he be looking for us? One thing's always going through my mind, self preservation. You could be crouching down, kneeling with a patient, concentrating on them and the gunman could come back to finish them off, make a proper job of it. And what does he find? Two ambulance men resuscitating his victim. He's not going to be very pleased with us, is he?

We went in to see the dead man's wife. She was in a terrible state but didn't want to go to hospital. There were neighbours looking after her, but when the doctor had certified the victim's death we thought it would be sensible to ask the doctor to talk to her. He confirmed she was physically all right, gave her some sedatives, and our job was done. Except that as soon as it had become apparent that there'd been a murder, the whole world descended on the location: forensic, the incident unit, armed response teams and the chiefs all turned up with their vehicles. All this in a small, very narrow cul-de-sac, so our ambulance was hemmed in. We were all in a state of shock. What we'd seen was horrific. We took the policewoman in the back of our ambulance and just talked to her. We'd been told about a shooting so we were semi-prepared but she wasn't.

It would have been good to have got away from the situation, got on with something else, but we were there for nearly five hours. Apparently the police had found a cartridge under our ambulance so we couldn't move it anyway. The neighbours were pretty good, and gave us cups of coffee, but it was not a good night.

Guns frighten the living daylights out of me, and most ambulance people. We'd just come on shift, about seven o'clock on a summer's evening, when we got a similar call.

'There's been a shooting incident in the Tyne Valley beyond Ryton, we don't know where, but apparently the place is on fire, so head for the smoke.'

I was with the same colleague who'd been at the previous shooting. We got to Ryton in five minutes and in the distance we could see the smoke. The police helicopter was swooping around and, as we approached the scene, there were police cars abandoned in the middle of the road. We had just enough room to get past them. I said to my mate, 'If there's any sign of a bloke with a gun, we're legging it. And if the bloke jumps out in front of us and points his gun we're going for him, we'll run him over.' I wouldn't have thought twice about it either.

When we eventually found a policeman we learnt that the gunman had just come out of prison and had come back to this caravan park to get his old job back. But he'd been turned away. This had upset him so he'd set the place on fire, then shot someone in the leg and run off into the woods. Another crew had arrived before us and taken away the chap who'd been shot, which left us as back up for the police, in case anybody else got in the way of a bullet. The firearms squad arrived and still nobody knew what was going on. Most unnerving of all, nobody had any idea where the gunman was.

The police asked us to go to a rendezvous point at a nearby junior school and wait, but when we got there nobody was around. I tell you, it was eerie. I thought, knowing my luck, if this gunman turns up anywhere he's going to be at this junior school. The search went on and we were there most of the night. No one had arranged food or even tea so there we were in the middle of the countryside starving. It didn't help the nerves. The gunman was found eventually in a corn field not far from us. He was surrounded by police marksmen, and he gave himself up.

RIGHT: *The schoolboy being moved on our carrying chair.*

11:47 AM

IT WAS OUR morning for educational establishments. We were off to another leg injury at a large senior school in the north of Newcastle. We drove to the front entrance and made our way to the receptionist. She didn't know exactly where the boy was, so had to 'phone around. He was eventually located in the PE block. He'd been playing football in the gym and his leg had gone into a spasm. It had happened before and when he'd seen his doctor, he'd been told he'd grow out of it. He hadn't! The PE teacher, who seemed a quiet man, was very helpful and suggested that rather than carry the boy, who was in a lot of pain, through the school it might be better if we brought the ambulance round to the back of the sports block by a track which was difficult to find because it was hardly ever used. While Karen stayed with the boy, the teacher jumped in the front of the ambulance

and directed me around the back of the playground. As we rounded the corner of a building we saw three of his pupils skiving and smoking. They were gobsmacked. It was enough of a surprise to see an ambulance there, but the last person they expected to see sitting in the front was their PE master. He wound the window down and really gave them what for, bellowing at them. To say they jumped would be an understatement. They got the fright of their life. It took me back to my own days behind the cycle shed!

Like the previous patient, we put the boy's leg in our box splint and took him to the hospital where we left him waiting to be treated.

Every ambulance person's heart sinks at the prospect of 'the long walk'. We were once sent on a call where someone had rung from a roadside call box to say that a motor cyclist had come off his bike at a rally cross event being held in and around a disused quarry. Someone would meet us at the entrance and direct us. It had been a long hot day, it was now half an hour from the end of our shift and we were knackered. Sure enough, the people were there on the roadside, and they directed us to a marshal further on along a dust track. I asked where the accident was and the marshal pointed, 'You see them little dots up by the far side of the quarry?' I could see the road we were on went as far as a group of people in the distance. The man continued, 'That's as far as the road goes and the biker is beyond them by the people who look like even smaller dots.'

When we stopped by the first group I did one of the most comprehensive sessions of 'Did anyone see what happened?' and 'Where has he hurt himself?' that I have ever done. The patient was just about discernible in the distance across the rough terrain that had presumably attracted the bikers in the first place. I got as much information as possible about the casualty's condition, and deduced that he'd probably broken his leg. So I selected the relevant splint, my mate carried the analgesic gas and we persuaded a couple of willing spectators to help carry the stretcher. I had to hope to God that I was right with my long distance diagnosis. It took us ages to get there, but I was right, he had broken his leg. After we had put the splint on, we then had to carry him over all this rough ground for nearly a mile back to the ambulance. We were all absolutely knackered. When we got him in the ambulance we were all huffing and puffing like an OAPs' outing. I said to him, 'Right, we're going to sit down now, you can drive!' He took that in good heart and I must say he seemed to appreciate that he'd caused us a lot of bother and was full of thanks. He did however make the mistake of asking if we'd brought the bike back as well.

12:15 PM

A STRAIGHTFORWARD URGENT call to an elderly lady who'd had a stroke. A doctor had been to see her and contacted our Control to ask if we could take her in to hospital within two hours for a checkup. When we got to the area we found that the whole estate was called by one name and the numbers didn't run in any logical order. I would not have been happy had this been an emergency, it took us ages. She was very pleased to see us, and even she said the numbering was 'daft'. We took her straight to hospital.

13:00 PM

WE RADIOED IN to say we were clear and Control told us to return to the station and try to get a meal break. For once we had a bit of time, so it was feet up on the recliner and a chance to have a chat to the other crew on station. But that didn't last long because the red 'phone went and they were on their way, and we had the duty room to ourselves.

One of the facts of our job in the accident and emergency section of the ambulance service is that we are rarely in the same place with any number of our colleagues for any length of time. The work load and the shift patterns mean that you can go for weeks without seeing the same people. One of the few times we were able to meet and talk was during the ambulance dispute which in every other sense was a bitter and dark time within the service.

The dispute really started in the winter of 1989 and it was nationwide. Ambulance people in general are not militant, but they like to see fair play. We had the feeling that we were being outdone by other emergency services and were falling behind with pay. After paramedic training, and all the extra responsibility that entails, we were not paid any extra. Throughout the country there were mass meetings which were unusual events, and to be at one of these gatherings was quite something. There was a great sense of camaraderie. In the end, with the public very much on our side, we won the day. There have been a number of changes since then. For instance the Northumbria Ambulance Service (NAS) has become a self-governing trust, which has meant changes for staff in many areas.

Since the reforms in the health service the NAS is much more open to the dictates of the market. We have to fight for contracts with all the hospitals, and to do that we have to be efficient and competitive. This has meant changes in the way we work – our shift pattern, for example. Shifts used to be eight hours, now it's twelve which I prefer. It means we work four days one week and three the next, leaving a good amount of time at home. In the wider view, the NAS has to look for new opportunities for making money to pump into the service. Schemes such as making our workshops available to service private cars, or providing first-aid training for Newcastle's factories or club bouncers, all bring in extra finance. There are detractors and supporters of the political drive towards trust status in the health service in general, only time will tell who's right.

13:34 PM

WE TEND TO find that types of injuries come in runs. Today legs were top of the chart. This emergency call was to a lady in Throckley, on the other side of town. So we had to battle through Newcastle to get to her. She was an elderly lady whose bones must have been brittle. She'd gone over on her ankle, and had snapped her tibia and fibula. The jagged end of the bones had pierced the underlying muscle and skin and were now protruding about two inches. This had happened in the street, yet somehow, she had managed to crawl back to her house, unlock the door and call for an ambulance.

There was blood everywhere but, unbelievably, she complained of very little pain. We get big hulking hard men who get a knock and scream the place down. I should know I'm the same. This old lady was really plucky, very calm and we warmed to her. We put a sterile dressing onto her exposed bone and another bandage over that because the blood was coming through. We then splinted her leg and supported her foot. Karen brought the wheeled trolley into the house and we lifted her gently on to it. This must have been painful for her, but she didn't make a sound. In the ambulance we made her comfortable, gave her oxygen and decided to put an intravenous drip up to replace the fluid she had lost. She was chatting all the way to Newcastle General where we left her, still smiling despite her injuries.

14:21 PM

WE RECEIVED A call to go as back up to another central ambulance that had been sent to a road accident. The details were vague, except that we knew it involved a crane. As we drove down the street we followed a line of people leaving their houses to walk down towards the flashing lights of the ambulance and police cars. It appeared to be quite an attraction. When we pulled up we saw that a crane had somehow toppled over on to a passing car which had been

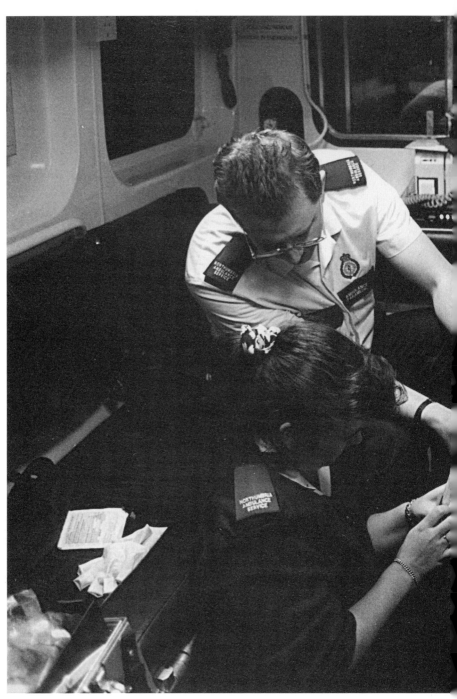

ABOVE: Inserting a needle to set up an intravenous drip.

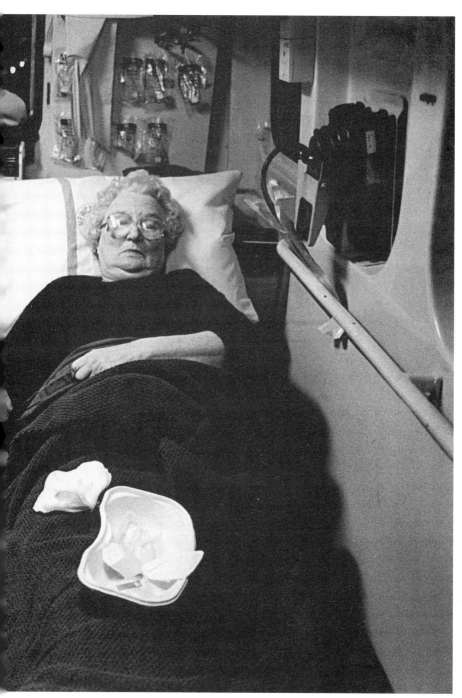

OVERLEAF: Car and crane after a miraculous escape.

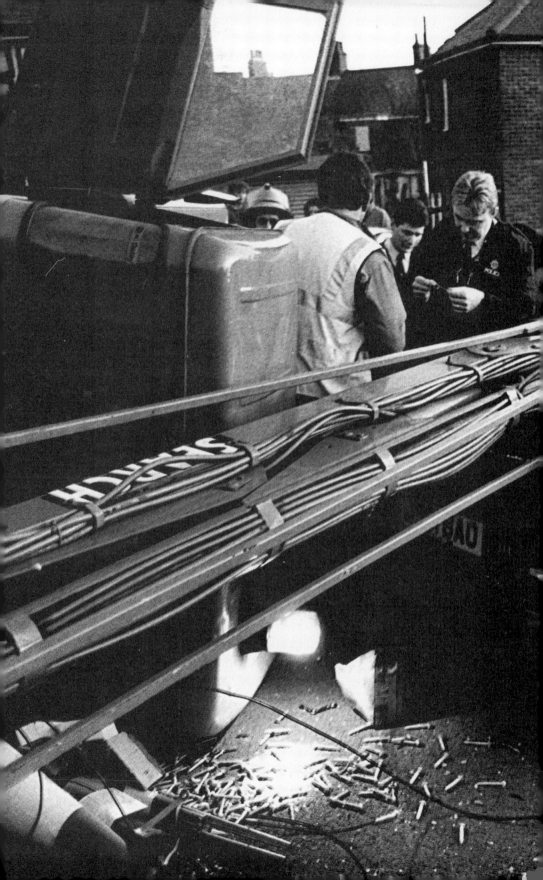

quite severely flattened. I spoke to Chris, the paramedic from the first crew on scene. He told me that when they'd arrived the occupant of the damaged car was sitting stunned, surrounded by what had been his car. The crane had smashed down onto the roof at an angle which left only the driver's seat undamaged. The driver had had the luckiest escape imaginable. God had been looking after his own. The driver was now in the ambulance with Chris who was replacing his dog collar with a cervical collar.

Our first task at any road accident is not to treat the patient, but to assess and eliminate the risk of further danger to them or to ourselves. There is no sense in climbing into a car to help someone and being killed by a heavy lorry running into the vehicle. So you must arrange a warning. At the very least a triangle, but preferably a vehicle between the accident and oncoming traffic.

The second priority is the care of the patient. You can either take the danger away from the patient or the patient away from the danger. In a road accident for instance, the car may be on fire. If you're the first of the emergency services on the scene and the car is blazing away, you have to make a calculated judgement about trying to get someone out, because you could easily become a victim yourself. You may have to rip them out literally and injure them even more. But a live person without a leg is better than somebody who is dead and intact. Common sense will dictate.

Whenever possible though, you do not move them until they have been thoroughly examined, because a lot of people involved in road accidents get whiplash or back injuries. So it's very important to try and stabilize their neck and back in the position you find them. If they are not breathing then, of course, resuscitation becomes the priority. If they're not trapped you pull them out of the car, but quite often they will be, so you can only recline the seat, create as much room as possible by opening the rear door, climb in and commence CPR.

I don't think there's any scientific reasoning behind it, but it's very rare to find an accident involving two people in a car where both are seriously hurt or both perfectly all right. Usually one is injured. The worst scenario for me is where one has been killed, even decapitated and the other is all right, but trapped alongside them. They could be there for a long time with someone they loved.

We had an incident where a packed coach had struck a car sideways on. The passenger, a young lad, was trapped by his leg which looked broken, and was drifting in and out of consciousness. The driver, a girl, was in a far worse condition. She was pinned by both her legs, but more importantly she was not breathing and had no pulse. We needed to start resuscitating her. I was able to recline her seat and make her horizontal even though her legs were trapped. I then climbed in the back and began resuscitating her. The coach had almost nosed its way inside the car so it was a very confined area.

My partner jumped on the coach to check for any other injuries. They were all a little dazed but no one was physically hurt. The driver was really badly shaken but refused to go to hospital. The coach behind (they'd been travelling in convoy) was driven by his brother who said that he'd look after him.

There were so many onlookers that the firefighters put a tarpaulin around the car so that we could work without being gauped at. All the time, while I was working on the girl the firemen were cutting away to free her legs. They also cut off the back of the car, which was a hatchback, to give me more room.

They then freed the passenger's legs and my mate got the lad out and dealt with him. He was in deep shock, not only from his leg injuries but from the realization of what was going on. I managed to establish an airway for the girl and carry on CPR. The sweat was pouring off me through the physical exertion of carrying out chest compressions. I did everything I could for her, but she didn't survive. She was in her early twenties with her whole life ahead of her. Later on, when I made enquiries, I found out that she had broken her neck and would have died instantly. I can't help thinking that the young lad will be haunted forever by the experience of being trapped beside his girlfriend like that.

14:42 PM

WE WEREN'T REQUIRED at the crane incident so headed back to base. Halfway back we were given another road accident. The police had been pursuing a stolen vehicle which had hit a parked car. When we arrived there were no patients to be treated. They'd fled the scene.

A couple of years back we were always getting calls to joyriders who'd smashed themselves up. Most times their mates had pulled them out and they were away before we arrived, but one night Control told us that a policeman had been involved in an accident with two joyriders who were trapped. I'm afraid I don't have much feeling for joyriders, nor do most ambulance people. But if they are injured, then we deal with them like anyone else. It was about one in the morning when we got there. Both cars had finished up in a graveyard. Overhead a police helicopter beamed it's searchlight down on the scene. It's down draught was blowing the branches of the trees, making the whole scene flicker like an old film. This made for a very surreal atmosphere.

We carried out triage on the three injured and discovered that the joyriders were more seriously hurt than the policeman, though none of them were in too bad a way. The two joyriders were both trapped in the car by their legs so we had to wait for them to be cut out. The police explained that they'd taken a top-of-the-range sports car and were doing 80 mph in a 30-mph area when they hit the police car. The stolen car was surrounded by policemen as they were cut out. There was no way those kids were going to escape. We were nearly three miles away from the Tyne, yet they'd even got a police launch out in case they'd headed for the river. It seemed as though more police and fire brigade were arriving every minute. By the time we came to treat the policeman so many of his colleagues were asking if he was all right, or could they do anything that they were getting in the way of us treating him. Thankfully he was only suffering from whiplash. I put his neck in a collar and he was taken to hospital in another ambulance.

When I first asked the two boys if they were OK I was

firmly told to mind my own business in colourful terms! They then flung a stream of abuse at us and the police in particular. They were putting on the big toughies act. After they'd been freed we took them onto the ambulance and treated their cuts and bruises. In the ambulance they both started to pretend they were in a worse condition than they actually were, presumably thinking that it might help their case, or at least evoke some sympathy. One faked unconsciousness. What he didn't realize was that if a patient is really in such a bad way that there's a danger of them stopping breathing, we have to insert an airway, a tube, into their mouth and slightly down their throat to ensure that the airway is kept clear. You normally assess the patient's size and choose a tube which is not too big or small. However, there's no better way known to paramedics to confirm that your patient really is ill than to choose an airway just slightly larger than is really needed. Even the most determined faker can't cope with that. The first lad gagged and let us know in no uncertain terms that he was very much conscious. The second lad obviously heard what was going on and suddenly decided that he wasn't so bad after all.

By the time we got them to hospital they'd stopped playing games and swearing at us. They became the young lads they really were. Wrapped in blankets which enveloped them like babies, they sobbed and cried. But they could easily have been two young boys who'd killed a policeman.

16:14 PM

WE WERE SENT off on a call to someone who'd fallen on a bus. The location we were given was the three-mile long perimeter road of an estate. Of course we didn't have the number of the bus and, as sod's law would have it, there were scores of them. I think they'd come out to find us! We stopped at one bus, then another, then another and on the fourth, a lady with a child flagged us down. The child didn't belong to her, but she had seen him being bullied on the bus. The poor lad had a black eye, a bloody nose and his school uniform had been covered in mud. He looked very forlorn standing there sniffling. She told us that he seemed to have been picked on for no apparent reason. I would like to think this was an isolated incident, but it's not, because we get quite a few calls to victims of bullies. Of course they are not only children.

We informed our Control of what had happened. As the lady was a witness we took her name and address. The lad lived en route to the hospital so I asked Control to clear it that we could call via his home to collect one of his parents, and that they should ask the police to meet them at the hospital. When we knocked on the door his mother answered. She had her slippers on, curlers in and was smoking a fag. She was really taken aback. I explained everything to her while she was putting on her coat. When we got to the hospital they checked the lad over, but there was nothing seriously wrong.

The call that really sends a chill through your spine is a road accident which involves a child. Some time ago we had a report that a child had been knocked over on his bicycle and was possibly under the car. When we got to the road the light was fading but we could see that the car was on top of a child's bike, and there was no one in the car. My first thought was that the driver had done a runner because he or she had killed the child. Straight away that got the adrenaline going. I grabbed my bag and jumped down to look under the car. I could see the bike and on the far side what indeed looked like a badly crumpled body. As I jumped up and ran around the other side a man sauntered over.

'You looking for the boy?'

Panic over. He and the driver had been taken away into a house. To make doubly sure I got down on my knees and looked under the car again. Sure enough the bike was underneath, but the shape was the red pannier bags. People looking underneath in the fading light could easily have thought it was a small body. We went in to the house and checked him over, but apart from a few cuts and bruises, he was just a bit shaken.

I've been at other road accidents where children have

been seriously injured. Just when you're doing your best to resuscitate them, their parents arrive and are wild with anxiety. They desperately want to pick up their little daughter who looks ashen and hold her. This is where bystanders are vital; they have to keep them from us and the child. If the parent suddenly picks their child up, they could kill or seriously injure them. But how terrible it must be to see your own child fading away, with a total stranger pumping their chest. What a terrible final image of your daughter or son to have to carry forever.

17:08 PM

THERE IS NO easy answer to the calls to our regulars, because the day we do not respond will be the day one of them will die of neglect. We are in a double bind, we don't want to pick them up because they are wasting our time and possibly delaying us from attending a real emergency, yet they are part of the fabric of our society, therefore part of our concern. Most of them we know by name. We certainly knew the chap who was causing problems at the Advice Centre tonight. As we got out of the ambulance we could hear him bellowing away, complaining about his rights. He'd obviously spent all his money on drink and thought the Advice Centre should give him some more.

The centre was very busy with people genuinely wanting help, but they were being intimidated by this man's violent behaviour. We were directed to an office where four members of the staff were trying to calm him down. There was certainly nothing medically wrong with him, in fact I was wondering why the centre had called us, rather than the police. He had, however, told one of the staff that he had a mental problem and that if they didn't help him, he would commit suicide. We, of course, had been hearing that story for years, but the centre hadn't and wisely they had called us. Eventually we managed to persuade him to come with us, but when he got outside, he homed in on an empty beer bottle at the side of the road, picked it up and began to threaten us with it. We don't fight anger with anger and just backed off, while still talking to him in a calm voice. He then hurled the bottle at the ambulance along with a string of obscenities and ran off. I certainly wasn't going to run after him.

18:01 PM

GETTING TOWARDS THE end of a quiet day a call came in with a report of a RTA on the Shields Road. It's a very long road which goes from Newcastle to the coast, with house numbers well up into the thousands. As we were heading through the rush hour traffic, we asked Control for a more accurate location and they were able to give a number. When we arrived outside the house, there wasn't anything that looked remotely like a road traffic accident. We knocked at the address we'd been given and a middle-aged lady explained to us that she had heard a bang, looked out of her window and seen that a car had buried itself in a garden opposite. As soon as she'd heard the noise she assumed there'd been a road traffic accident and had phoned 999. She hadn't wasted any time and in fact could well have saved a life by her promptness. However, within the minutes we had taken to get there, the car had driven off. She was apologetic about wasting our time, but we assured her, very sincerely, that she had done the right thing and told her not to hesitate to call us if anything happened in the future.

We had a similar non-event recently on a lay-by off the A1. Someone with a mobile 'phone had spotted this chap slumped over his wheel and he wisely 'phoned to pass on the information. When the ambulance arrived, blue lights flashing and sirens blazing, the collapsed man awoke from a deep sleep.

When you've just finished your basic ambulance training you're desperate to get out there and to have the opportunity to try out your skills at a major RTA with masses of trauma. Every time a call comes in, you speed off hoping that it will be something juicy which you can get stuck in to. It might sound callous and macabre, it isn't. It's simply that you know you're going to come across one at some point and you want to get on with it and put into practice all your hard learned theory.

Not long after I was let loose on an unsuspecting public, I was sent on an emergency call to a road accident near Hexham, out in rural Northumbria. I hadn't seen a fatal RTA and it was in the back of my mind that this might be the one. The call gave the position as somewhere on a particular road. Often on these back roads there are few landmarks and what few there are can be hard to pin point. But the lad on with me was a local and knew the area well. It was just after chucking out time and he reckoned they'd have been on a pub crawl. So he worked out the most likely point on the stretch of the road between two pubs. Then he started applying his local knowledge. It was 'left here, down about a mile and they'll be right by the farm', and he was spot on. They'd swerved on a sharp bend, smashed down a farm fence and ended upside down in the middle of the field. The cows had wandered out through the gap onto the road so we ended up doing a 'Wyatt Earp at the old ranch' impersonation before we could get into the field.

While my colleague radioed in our exact location I jumped out and walked across to the van. My torch was fairly dim and produced more of a glow than a beam. Nevertheless I shone it into the cab. There was no one there. So I moved around the van, shining the torch ahead of me. Coming round to the other side I saw a body lying there covered in blood from head to foot. Blood was all over the grass and all over the back doors of the van. It was everywhere. Horrific. I remember thinking that the reality was more frightening than the image I'd had, what was I going to do?

I pulled myself together and thought I'd better see if he was breathing. I knelt down and shone my torch on his face. His eyes opened, registering me with difficulty and he slurred out, 'Thank God your here.'

I nearly dropped with fright. This was something out of a horror movie. He had to be dead, he was covered in so much blood.

My training came into operation. I asked if he was hurt anywhere.

'I'm all right, mate, apart from me leg.'

I couldn't believe that all this red stuff was coming from one wound, but a quick examination of the rest of him revealed no obvious injuries except for a broken leg which wasn't bleeding. As I was moving around to look again I kicked something metal. It was an open can of red oxide paint.

The van belonged to a decorating firm and he'd been sitting in the back surrounded by tins of the stuff. When the van had turned over the whole lot had been flung across the van and some of the cans had blown open. His mates, probably all drunk, had started to help him out but then run off and left him with a broken leg. I think he was too drunk to care. I had to lean up against the van to regain my composure for quite a few minutes.

The first fatal accident I attended was quite some time after the red paint job. We were passed details of a serious RTA on the A68. Two cars, one person dead. Another ambulance was also on its way. It was a freezing winter's night, pitch dark, with driving sleet. As we got closer I began to get very nervous, wondering if I would cope, or make a balls-up in front of everyone. Then I started getting anxious about where I'd put the equipment, the splints, the bandages and so on. I had a real panic attack.

I saw the road barrier erected by the police and realized I would be in action any minute. The people at the crash wouldn't know how inexperienced I was, they expected someone who knew what he was doing and they'd be getting me. By the time we got round the corner to the crash I had several hundred butterflies in my stomach and a very tight chest. It turned out to be a classic two-car, head-on crash where one of the drivers had been killed. However, the other crew were doing their damnedest to resuscitate him. The person in the other car was trapped by his feet but was not badly hurt and was being looked after by a policeman. As soon as I got out of the ambulance my fear disappeared and the adrenaline started pumping very fast.

All I wanted to do was get straight into the resuscitation, put my training into practice, see what somebody who had been injured in a bad road accident looked like. But it was not to be. I was asked to look after the lad in the other car and felt really let down. I splinted his legs, but I wasn't in the front line where the real action was. There was no real hope of bringing the other man back and before long a local doctor arrived to certify death. Then one of the other crew asked me to check in their ambulance to see if, by mistake, he'd picked up any of our equipment. Of course in the ambulance was the dead man. That was the first time I'd ever seen anybody who'd been killed as the result of a car crash. He looked quite peaceful as though he was asleep. I'd broken the duck, the fear had been vanquished.

18:15 PM

WHEN THE FIRE alarm is activated in a hospital, the ambulance service automatically gets a call from the fire service to attend. In this case it was a call to one of the large hospitals in Newcastle. When we got there, we liaised with the senior fire officer, who told us it was a false alarm and we could stand down and return to base.

The problem with every alarm call is that you have to assume it's going to be the one where everything really does happen. We regularly get called to Newcastle airport. There's a special line from the control tower to our Control, who must hate it when it flashes. For Control it means the headache of releasing a minimum of six ambulances to travel to the airport and wait until the aeroplane in trouble has landed. It usually looks like a convention of the emergency services. A line of ambulances next to a line of fire engines and police cars all round the perimeter of the airfield closing the roads. Luckily, so far there's never been a major incident. Usually the problem is something simple like a warning light on the aircraft's dashboard, but I always think what a nightmare it must be for the people on board the 'plane. The

A firefighter at tonight's false alarm.

captain will be trying to reassure the passengers that they have a minor problem, yet when they look out of the window all they can see are masses of fire engines, ambulances and police cars, blue lights flashing, racing towards the runway!

I have had one call to an air crash which was for real. We were told it was a 'plane which had gone down near the airport, with no further information. As we drove towards the spot we kept asking for more details, but they didn't have any. Eventually Control managed to get back to the person who'd reported it to ask for more information. He was the pilot of another aeroplane and had seen a small two-seater craft disappear behind some trees about a mile and a half from the airport. The only way we could get near the site was down a narrow muddy track, and when we reached the end we had to carry all our equipment across two fields. There were firemen running everywhere, chopping down fences and having a field day. When we got to the aircraft it was unscathed, the pilot said he was unhurt and that this crash was not as bad as the last one he'd had on the A1. I wondered what he had in mind for his third crash!

A couple of weeks later we got another call that an aircraft had crashed, this time into the hillside near Whickham. Initially, I thought it was some of the lads trying to wind me up. Then I saw my mate taking the call and he was shaking. All he said was, 'This is the big one, an aircraft has crashed.' Apparently the whole of the hillside was on fire and Control was sending Blaydon, the neighbouring station, in support. We got onto the A1 and were going at a fair rate of knots, when they overtook us. This meant all we had to do was follow them. We could see the clouds of smoke from the fire ahead of us. As we got nearer, I was convinced that it was a major 'plane crash. We drove up a track but had to stop when it started to turn away from the fire. I put the ambulance in reverse and we went down the track, in convoy, backwards. Eventually, we stopped a local out walking with his dog and asked him how we could get to the fire. He said he knew the way and jumped into the ambulance with his dog. It was already dark and there was smoke everywhere, we couldn't find the way and were becoming increasingly anxious. In the end we were spotted by a police car which led us to the site. We arrived at the same time as the fire brigade, to find that our 'plane crash was a haystack on fire. There was much relief all round.

Unfortunately not all our calls with the fire brigade are as innocuous. We had a call one night before Christmas to go to a fire at one of the tall blocks of flats in Gateshead. From a distance we could see the smoke rising and billowing. We were radioed with a message from the fire brigade telling us how to approach the flats. As instructed we took the route via a roadway which runs along the base of the flats and then walked up a ramp which led to the main entrance. Taking equipment and hard hats with us, Mark and I were met by a fireman who showed us where we were needed. He explained that the fire had started in a flat on the eighth floor and as the flames took hold a girl had jumped from the window. She'd hit a concrete flower container and bounced off that onto the ground where we found her. When we got to her she wasn't breathing. We gently turned her on her back and started to resuscitate her. As we were doing this the flames were still coming out of her flat and the heat was cracking the remaining glass which was falling around us. It was one of the most terrifying situations I'd ever been in, some of the glass was shaped like daggers.

I worked hard on the girl but sadly she had surgical emphysema. Her lungs had perforated, so that when I started to resuscitate her all the air I was pumping into her was escaping from her lungs and going under her skin. She simply started to blow up like a balloon. Within minutes she appeared to be twice the size she was when I started to resuscitate her. She just billowed out. It was an awful sight to see. There was nothing anyone could do for her. I kept thinking that she must have known that if she jumped she was most likely going to die. It was so far up, but she must have just weighed up the odds and thought there's no other way I'm going to get out, I'll jump. What really hurt was that when we examined her further I saw she was gripping something. I opened her hand and saw that it was a photograph. She had jumped out clutching a picture of her baby.

The day after the tower block fire I picked up the local newspaper and there on the front page was a photograph of the girl and a little bit about her background, her baby and about the fire. I couldn't read more than a few words, I had to turn the pages. I read the inside pages for a while then I went back to her story. There was a young, good looking girl, smiling out at me. I couldn't equate that smiling face with the body we'd found, hand gripping the photograph.

An old ambulance man, long since retired, said to me, 'You'll never remember the face of a dead person' and it's true. I can remember the places, the course of events, but I can't picture the face of any of the hundreds of dead bodies I've dealt with, except one. A call had come in from a man to say his mother had telephoned him in a desperate panic saying she was suffering a terrible pain in her chest. The man lived some way away and had called us. When we got to her place, an old mining house, her back door was unlocked so we went straight in. She was sitting there alone, quite dead. But I will always remember her face, it was fixed in an expression of absolute horror, her eyes were bulging out. It was a picture of total fear. Part of ambulance black humour and folklore is that anyone who dies in the pub has a smile on their face. In reality it's just that the muscles have relaxed after death. But this woman's face radiated terror especially from her eyes. They still haunt me.

I know it's part of our job to deal with death, but a death like hers, along with cot deaths or suicides, affect all paramedics. Even though the bottom line is, we're not God and can only do our best, we still desperately want to be able to achieve the impossible. The only consolation is that if I have done my best then I don't feel guilty.

18:58 PM

WHEN WE DROVE back into the station the next crew were ready to take over our ambulance so we did the usual checks, fuelled up, and for once at 7.00 p.m. Karen and I made our way promptly to the door.

After a real downer I tend to keep everything bottled up inside me. We discuss a case like that with our mates when we get back to the station, to try and talk it out a bit. If the next few jobs aren't too demanding we go back to it again. Even then after a twelve-hour shift in which you've dealt with incidents like the girl jumping, you have a few beers with the lads to unwind. Then you go home, and the images come back to you and you're like a bear with a sore head, perhaps you shout at the wife. Although you haven't told her anything you hope she understands. My best way of coping is to go to bed, sleep and try to forget it. But quite often I wake in the middle of the night and I'm back at the incident. I'm back there with, say, the cot death. I'm running for the door with the baby in my arms, but I'm not moving, I'm stuck in the same place screaming, lashing out and in a cold sweat. I have these nightmares, terrible realistic nightmares and I think a lot of others do to.

The last thing I want to do is to spew out all that's happened to my wife Claire and the family. I don't think it's fair to stress them with all the terrible details. I tend to bottle up the really bad ones. Then like a delayed reaction three or four days later, after I've had three or four pints and mulled the horror of it all over in my mind, and edited out the worst details, I'll mention it to Claire. On other occasions she'll be reading the paper and ask me if I heard about some terrible road accident and I'll realize I was there and talk a bit more about it. She knows now when part of my mind has gone into hibernation, she also knows that at some point I will tell her what I've been through.

One of the nightmares of all paramedics is that they will be called out to an incident that involves someone in their family. The nearest I've come to that was when my son Christopher was taken seriously ill. I was contacted at work and went into the same sort of state that we encounter in others – all to pot. Claire didn't want to call an ambulance and had taken Christopher by car to The Queen Elizabeth Hospital. That was ironic because I was on duty in the area and would probably have been given the call to pick up my own son. When I arrived at The Queen Elizabeth as a parent it was a strange experience. Christopher did not look at all well. Poor little lad, he was as white as a sheet and screaming. The doctor told us that they thought he had what is called an intussusception, effectively a block in the intestines. He was in shock which was causing him to come in and out of consciousness. He looked so pathetic, like a rag doll.

By the time I arrived it had been decided that it would be necessary to transfer Christopher to a specialist unit at the Royal Victoria Infirmary by ambulance. I was on with Stan who told them we had the ambulance outside. Stan told me to get in the back and off we went.

I made Christopher as comfortable as I could and tried to comfort Claire who was crying her eyes out. The whole atmosphere was so emotionally charged. Ordinarily the ambulance men would be reassuring the patient and the mother and father, but there wasn't an ambulance man to reassure me. I was the reassurer. Stan was really good, he took control and kept talking to us all during the drive. He said all the words I'd said a thousand times to patients. 'Nothing to worry about, we'll soon be there and when you are they'll look after him well.'

When we got to the hospital he added, 'By the way there's no need to come back to work Paul, don't even bother to 'phone. It's all in hand, we've sorted it out.'

It was a first-hand experience of how important reassurance is to a patient. Christopher was in the hospital for a week and made a full recovery, but it was a very worrying time for both of us. I was lucky, compared with Claire who had to sit and wait with him. Even though my work took me in and out of hospital all day long during that time, and even knowing that my son was up on one of the wards, I was somehow able to separate the two parts of my life. Although it was not an experience I would like to go through again, it was a great lesson in being on the other side of the service, and gave me an insight into how much difference the few right words can make.

— DAY —
THREE

06:30 AM

A HANDOVER FROM A weary night shift, saying we needed more equipment on the vehicle. They'd had a real rough, heavy shift dealing with drunks, violence and all the other delights of a night shift. From stores I booked out all the equipment we would need for the day, signed for the drugs and made sure all the paperwork was in order. Along with Karen, I checked the ambulance to make sure we were ready for the road. We were first out.

07:10 AM

OUR FIRST CALL was to a woman with chest pains whose condition was deteriorating. The address was opposite the road from one of our regular dialysis cases, so we knew exactly where the house was. When we got there, after a seven-minute drive, the front door was wide open. I knocked and shouted, 'Ambulance,' and a woman shouted, 'Yes, up here, quickly.'

Upstairs we found a sprightly lady sitting in bed being looked after by her daughter. So I said, 'Hello there, patient for the ambulance?'

The daughter replied, 'Yes, it's my Mum here.'

This morning's patient with chest pains.

Initially I wondered why we'd been called, she didn't appear to be deteriorating. But according to the daughter she was going downhill. She told us that her mother had developed a cold a couple of days earlier which had become worse, causing her to be a bit chesty. Now she was coughing quite heavily and having chest pains. She'd had a nitrate spray and this had relieved some of the pain. So thankfully the situation wasn't as bad as we had been led to believe. Understandably her daughter was anxious about her mother. It's easy for me to say you shouldn't panic, but probably in that situation I'd do the same. Stress effects people in different ways, some go all to pot yet others think logically.

We carried her down to the ambulance, gave her oxygen and put the electrodes on her chest. The monitor showed her heart was all right. We took her to the nearest casualty and left her feeling much happier now that she was surrounded by machines going bleep.

Every time we speed off to one of these calls to someone with chest pains we try to anticipate what we'll find, but every one is different. We got a call one Sunday morning to say that a chap was suffering chest pain. On a Sunday morning the roads are quiet, so we knew we'd be there in about eight minutes. We were about half way there when we had a message saying that the patient had stopped breathing. Jason really put his foot down then. When we reached the house I went straight in with our basic resuscitation equipment. The chap was lying on the settee in the living room. He wasn't breathing and he didn't have a pulse, so I started resuscitation. The settee was far too springy to attempt CPR and I had to move him onto the floor. His airway was clear, so I started to breathe for him using the bag and mask, then began CPR.

Jason followed in with all the advanced resuscitation equipment. I switched on the monitor and put one of the paddles on his sternum and the other on his apex, the side of the rib cage. The screen showed the patient was in VF, so I charged the machine up to 200 joules.

'Stand clear!' I delivered the shock but he was still in VF. I charged it up to 360 joules and delivered another shock but still the trace showed VF. I then charged it up for the third time. As I was doing all this I was aware that the relatives were leaning through the serving hatch and seeing their loved one being lifted six inches off the ground with a shock from the machine.

While I was trying to kick start him back to life I asked one of the family about his history. Apparently he had come home the previous day from the local hospital having recovered from open heart surgery. That evening he'd started having chest pains which had got worse during the night, so they got their doctor out at 4.00 a.m. He thought it was nothing to be concerned about and told them to put him to bed and make sure he rested. The bloke was feeling so uncomfortable and distressed that he couldn't make it upstairs so sat in the lounge. As the night wore on he became worse and his family called us, and his doctor, at about 7.00 a.m.

After I had delivered the third shock I followed protocol and intubated him, putting a tube down inside his windpipe and connected this up to the bag. I then gave him 200 mg of

Lignocaine and another shock, but he was still in VF. In between the shocks we continued doing CPR. I then gave him Adrenaline down the ET tube and followed this with another shock. Low and behold we got a pulse. His relatives were still leaning through the serving hatch calling out, 'How's he doing, is he breathing, will he be all right?' At the same time I was also trying to update Jason on what I was doing. Then a doctor arrived, but not the one who'd seen him earlier. This chap was a locum. He asked how we were doing and then sat on the settee to watch! On the final shock we got his heart going. I must have shouted something because this really got his relatives buzzing. I told the doctor we were going to take the chap to casualty. He smiled, agreed and stayed sitting.

All the relatives helped us out with our equipment. Although we had his heart going the man was still deeply unconscious and unable to breathe for himself. On the way to casualty I talked frankly to his wife and daughter about his prospects and what they should expect. I explained that when we got to the hospital, doctors and nurses would come onto the ambulance and they would ask questions about his history and what had happened. Also that they would be taken to a reception room where someone would take his details.

The hospital had a full resuscitation team standing by when we arrived. We worked with the hospital staff for about twenty minutes until they had stabilized his condition. We heard later that he had been transferred to the intensive care unit, but unfortunately the gentleman only lived for another hour. We had done everything possible. The man was effectively dead when we arrived at the house and we had succeeded in restarting his heart. But the pressures on his body from all the surgery he'd undergone were just too much.

08:00 AM

WE RADIOED IN that we were clear and Control came back straight away to say they had an urgent job for us. We

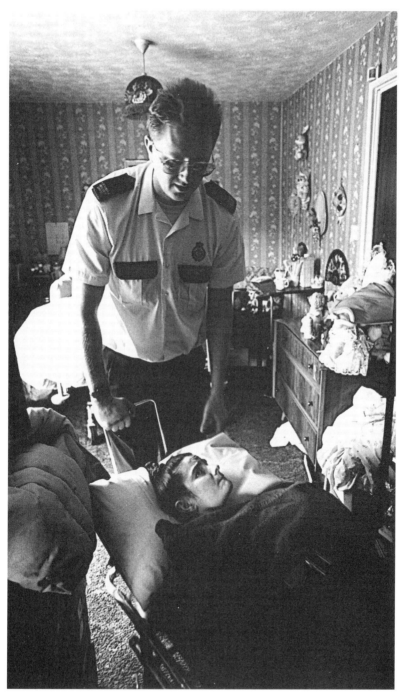

The patient on her way to physiotherapy.

had to pick up a handicapped girl who has regular physiotherapy. The problem was getting the ambulance close
enough to where she lived. When they designed some of the
estates, they never considered that people might need an
ambulance. It was a freezing cold day, with a bitter wind
which would have chilled the patient if we'd had to carry her
too far. We got in as close as we could and picked her up on
our stretcher from her downstairs bedrom. Her house was
nice and warm so we covered her in four blankets to maintain her body temperature. Although she could hardly speak
I kept chatting to her, just to reassure her.

08:35 AM

WE GOT OUR next job immediately, an emergency call to
a man who'd fallen through a glass door. There was some
confusion as to whether this was at a factory or a private
home. We knew the street but couldn't think of any factories
on it. During the four-minute drive our minds were filled
with the worst scenario: someone cut open or impaled on the
door. When we got to the street there were certainly no factories, so we queried the address which indeed turned out to
be a house. We were met on the drive by a neighbour who
explained that the gentleman was wobbly on his legs. He'd
been trying to get from one room to another and his legs had
given out, he'd fallen backwards and his head had gone
through the glass pane of the door. Immediately my thought
was that this was going to be grim. However, we found him
in the kitchen and straight away I could see he wasn't too
bad. His ear had a nasty cut and there was quite a lot of
blood. (Ears bleed heavily because there's a high concen-
tration of blood vessels beneath the surface of facial skin, as
seen when someone blushes.) We put a clean dressing and a
pressure pad on his wound, then a bandage around his head.
We gave him plenty of reassurance, because he was badly
shaken by the fall and advised his wife to get the glass
knocked out by a professional. Being a keen DIY person, I
felt like doing it myself, but I thought it would take up too

much time. From there on it was a straightforward job of taking him to the hospital to be checked over. He was a really nice old fellow, who had done a lot of voluntary work in the hospital. He couldn't thank us enough for coming out as quickly as we did.

Although this morning's case proved to be a genuine domestic accident, we're all wary of calls which sound as though they might be some sort of industrial case, particularly when they're a bit vague in their details. Despite the number of large industries like the shipyards and mining which have almost ceased to exist over the last few years in the North East, we're still an industrial area. Inevitably we get quite a lot of factory accidents and obviously some are worse than others. Quite often we receive a call to something innocuous which sounds like a faint. We're never surprised to find that the person has indeed fainted, but only because they've lopped part of their body off in some horrendous machine or other.

Since the tightening up of all the health and safety regulations companies have to call the police whenever there's a works accident. Inevitably some think that if they hide the true nature of the call they'll get away with it. However, we have to check that the police have been called, so they're wasting their time to try and cover it up.

We got a call one day – I can distinctly remember it was a clear, bright morning – to go to a metal-processing works. We had a real job to find the place. We drove up and down the road a few times but there weren't any signs for that factory. Although we'd both grown up in that area we just didn't have a clue where this particular building was. In the end after a lot of wasted time we drove into the most likely looking gate. There was no one around, so we wandered about and after what seemed like ages somebody said, 'Ay, what are you after mate?' We told him and he directed us to the manager's office, which is a bit too grand a description for what was not much more than a load of wooden crates knocked together decorated with a few girlie pictures on the wall. The only nod towards civilization was an old kettle boiling away on an industrial gas ring in the corner. The

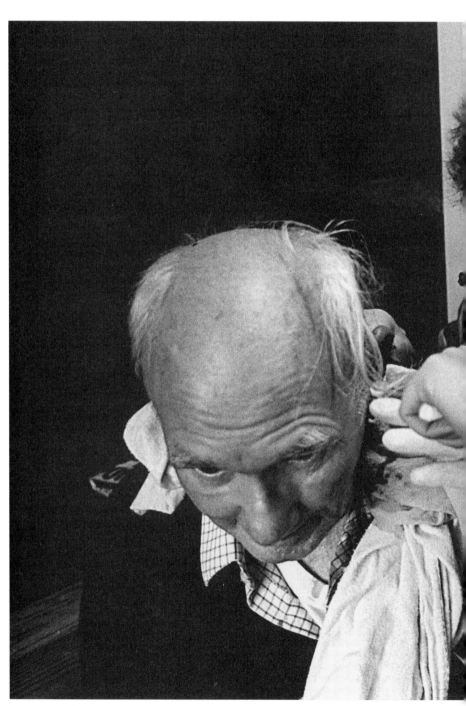

Removing glass splinters.

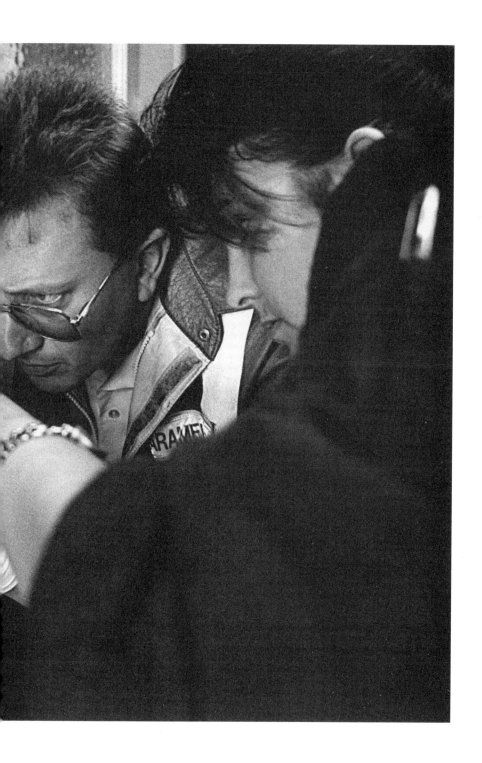

man we took to be the manager was sitting at his desk with a cigarette hanging out the corner of his mouth, getting on with his paperwork. A lad was sitting quietly in front of him, very white-faced with an old oily and blood-soaked rag wrapped around his hand. I asked the manager what had happened and he said, 'I think he's guillotined his hand off, but I'm not sure.' He was frighteningly matter of fact. We carried the lad out to the ambulance and asked what had happened. Once out of hearing of the boss he was keen to explain.

The firm took metal and cut it up into small pieces to be transported to a smelting plant. It was this lad's first morning and he'd been given ropy information on how to work the system. He'd been putting the bits of metal into the machine, pressing a pedal with his foot and holding onto the metal as an hydraulically operated guillotine thumped down cutting it in two. He'd been at it for a while and was getting speedy, putting the metal in, pressing the pedal, holding on, wallop, pulling it out. But this time he'd pushed the metal in too far, pressed the foot pedal and guillotined his hand.

We thought we should take a look in order to decide on our next action. Elevating his arm, we applied indirect pressure and took off the bandage. Surprisingly it had almost stopped bleeding. Half of his hand was hanging on by a piece of skin at the side just above the knuckles. We dressed it up and took him off to hospital. We could have put a drip up to replace fluid, but we didn't think he'd lost enough blood to warrant it. I don't know what happened to him because after we'd handed him over to casualty, Control was on the radio and off we went on another job.

About a month later we were at the ambulance station having a tea when the 'phone rang. It was a call to a wall collapse at a local concrete works near Blaydon, where a man was trapped. We had no idea how big a wall or how many injured there might be. Our divisional commander Arthur Lemin had been called to the scene to act as incident officer.

When we got there we were duly pointed towards what looked like a large water tank on stilts, some fifty or sixty feet up. There were several people waiting for us at the bottom and they told us that the injured lad was up inside the tank. They explained that it was some sort of holding tank for a coolant used in the processing. The sludge was poured in, the sediment allowed to settle and the liquid recycled. Every so often someone had to climb up into it to scrape away the build up of solidified sediment from the walls of the tank. One of the two lads who'd been doing it that morning had slipped and fallen. His mate had raised the alarm saying that the lad had hit his head, had sustained a large gash and, he thought, a broken arm.

I picked up the basic resuscitation gear and first aid equipment, and we stood at the base of the tower looking at the only way up, a series of vertical ladders linked by platforms. It was windy and the whole tower was moving and I'm not good at heights at the best of times. That day I was on with Jeff, who's an ex-fireman, and as we started to climb the first ladder he said to me, 'I don't fancy this one little bit.' Which really reassured me. I tried to put a brave face on it. I'd got the resuscitation gear in a bag in one hand and was holding on to the ladder with the other and being followed up by Arthur! The only thing that kept me going was the thought that I'd never live down a newspaper headline along the lines of 'Ambulance man with vertigo gets rescued by brave fireman'.

Up we went, higher and higher, with the wind getting stronger and stronger. Nevertheless we got up there and Arthur being the boss said, 'I'll go first and examine the patient.' The only way in to the chamber was through a small inspection hatch. It's not for me to comment on the waistline of a senior officer, but it would be fair to say that Arthur would probably not be in danger of being considered anorexic. I thought we had the makings of another headline, 'Second ambulance man stuck in rescue attempt.' There was no way he could get through. My waistline was not much different, but by breathing in I could just squeeze through. I stretched my arms ahead of me and wriggled in as best I could. The only light inside came through the inspection hatch, so it was blotted out as I climbed in. How anyone had managed to work in there I don't know. I stood in what must have been three feet or more of filthy sludge. There was more light coming in now through the inspection chamber and I was able to see the lad who was propped up against the chamber wall, holding his arm. He also had a nasty cut to his head. Arthur kept putting his head in saying, 'Do you need any help?' And I kept saying words to the effect of, 'I'm fine but could you please let some light in'.

I reassured the lad and dressed the gash. We decided the only way to get him out through the hole and down the tower was by strapping him securely to our paraguard rescue stretcher. Arthur and my colleague had somehow managed to manhandle the stretcher up the tower and pass it into the chamber. Despite the lack of space, with a fellow workman on the other side of him we somehow managed to strap the lad on and feed the stretcher out through the inspection chamber. This had all taken some time, during which the fire brigade had arrived with a turn table ladder. They transferred our stretcher across onto the turntable and strapped it on. He was then lowered swiftly to the ground.

Our descent was slower. With Arthur's diminutive frame hovering above me we took our time. When we arrived at the hospital, the lad didn't seem too bad. He soon recovered and sent me a nice thank you letter which finished up saying that he'd buy me a pint sometime. He must drink in one of the few pubs I don't frequent, because I'm still waiting!

A large number of calls to factories involve back injuries. They're seldom easy to deal with, need careful handling and therefore take a long time. With any injury to the back we're always over cautious about moving the patient in case there's any spinal damage. Our job is to keep the body in the same position as we find it, immobilize the patient as much as possible to make sure no more damage is done, get them into the ambulance and take them to hospital where the specialists can take over.

We had quite a tricky case in November at a wood fabrication works. When we arrived there was somebody on the gate to show us where to go. That was a good sign, it showed concern, co-operation and saved us valuable time. The chap who'd hurt himself was on all fours on a raised platform about five feet high and surrounded by railings. The railings acted as guards against the machinery which continued to clink and clang away around him. Nothing was going to stop the business. In fact the main workforce was getting on as usual, just a few of the lads were standing around looking concerned. Apparently this man had lent over to pick up a light box and when he'd gone to straighten up been hit by the most awful pain in his back. He'd probably just over-stretched and badly pulled his back muscles, but it was an awkward situation. The metal stairs leading up to the plat-form were no more than eighteen inches wide, the platform itself not much larger than about three feet by five. There was not much room to examine him, let alone move him onto a stretcher. I was pretty confident that from the description of what had happened and the examination that it was a muscular problem, but even so ideally I would have liked to have been able to lay him on his side on a stretcher, keeping him in the same position as we found him. But the guard rails all around the small platform prevented us. So we strapped his legs together to immobilize them as much as we could, and had to try to lift him onto our chair. Every time he tried the slightest move he screamed out in absolute agony. We stopped again to give him some analgesic gas but he was still in terrible pain. He was a heavy man, a good fourteen or fifteen stones and not at all easy to get down the stairs.

In the ambulance we propped him up on the bed using blankets to keep his legs in the same bent position. To judge by the look on his face and his screams you'd have thought he was in big trouble. We handed him over to the nurse at the hospital and carried on with our next job. A couple of hours later we were back at the casualty department and saw him walking out. It was quite a shock. When we had a chat with him he explained that they'd given him some strong painkillers to relax him and he'd been left to rest. Now he could walk, albeit with difficulty.

Not all work accidents happen in big factories and involve machinery. A few weeks ago we attended a young lad who was trapped under a filing cabinet. You automati-cally laugh, it's like something out of a silent movie. I mean, who gets trapped under a filing cabinet? Someone really weighed down by bureaucracy perhaps? We duly arrived at the location, a nursing home, where this lad had been cleaning the floors with a carpet cleaner. He'd been too conscientious and decided to clean under the filing cabinet. As he attempted to pull it away from the wall, the whole thing had tumbled down on him. He'd twisted as he'd fallen and the filing cabinet landed on his back. For once it was a nice big light room so we could see and move. The lad was face down with his head supported by his arms. We asked him his name, where he hurt and told him that we'd look after him. We always assume the worst, then you can't go wrong. He was in absolute agony with pain in the centre of his back. With back injuries time is not of the essence. It doesn't matter how long it takes – all day if needs be – the main object is not to change the position of the patient.

When we examined him first we found he had middle to lower back pain, and in the top of the lumbar area he had severe pain. I gently pinched his feet and the good news was that he still had sensation in his legs. If someone has badly damaged the spine the extent of any paralysis can be judged quickly by how much of their body is without feeling. But damage can still be done if the person is moved without care. The big fear is that a bone break can tear the spinal cord, causing paralysis. So we immobilized him by strapping his legs together and put a cervical collar round his neck. We used an orthopaedic 'scoop' stretcher for this job. It's aluminium so it's light. It's also adjustable for length and splits in two down the centre so you can gently slide each half under the body and clip them together without having to move them too much. With this lad we split it lengthways, got one half under his left leg and upper body, then gradually got the other section under his right side and clipped the stretcher together. In effect we hadn't changed his position, but we could now carry him out. Once he was strapped on, we lifted him out to the ambulance with the assistance of the police, who'd been notified by the home's manager because it was a work injury. We got him to hospital and they x-rayed him before moving him. He was lucky, he'd only bruised his back, and he left later that day.

09:10 AM

As we were leaving the casualty department we were asked to go back for a patient. Most people who get treatment at casualty departments have to make their own way home. This person had a full length leg plaster and had to lie down. Casualty could hardly ask him to go home by cab, so we were justifiably called in to take him home.

09:40 AM

It was a morning for urgent calls, this next one to a woman with pneumonia. Control had been contacted by this lady's doctor who wanted her taken in for observation. When we arrived we were let in by her friend. It was an interesting house, every door was painted with bright red gloss and the carpet was yellow. The lady was in her seventies and a nicer person you couldn't hope to meet. She explained she hadn't been well for some time. She couldn't get warm, was shivering and had a very chesty cold. We made her comfortable in the ambulance, sat her up so she could breathe better and dropped her off at the hospital.

10:15 AM

Yet another urgent call to an ankle injury. Again a doctor had requested we bring in one of his patients. We had to check the address in our *A–Z*. We found a short cut and were there in about ten minutes. As we pulled up at the house we saw the lady locking her front door, hobbling down the path to meet us. I said, 'Hello, what's the problem?'

She said, 'It's my left ankle, I twisted it about four days ago, had my doctor out, and he said I needed to go to hospital to get it x-rayed.'

OVERLEAF: *Transferring our patient to a hospital bed.*

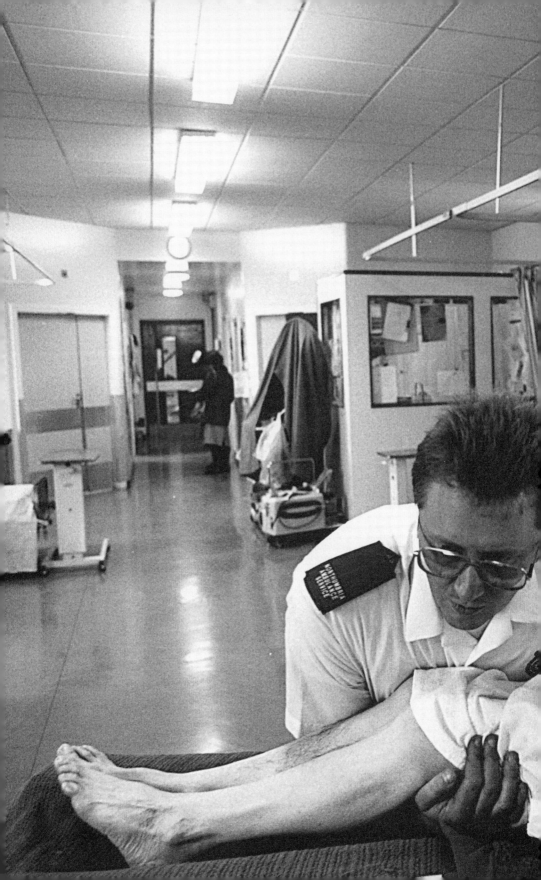

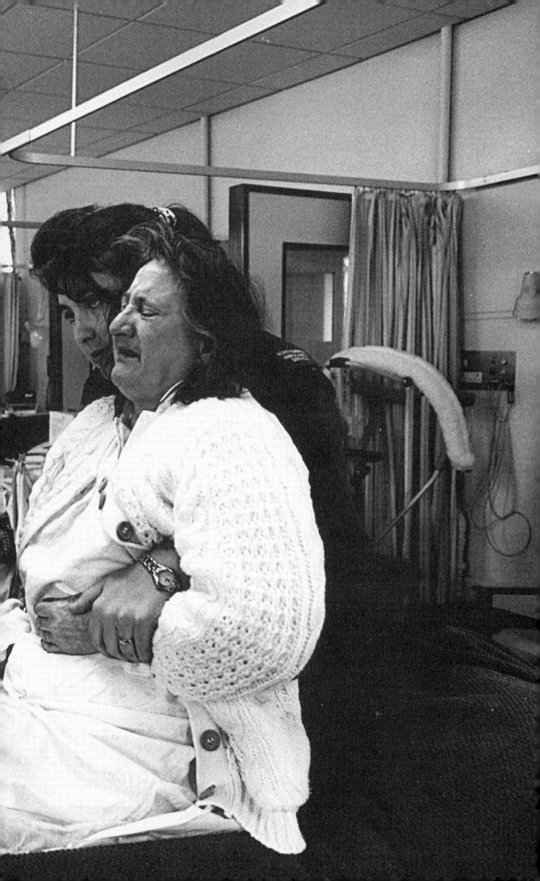

I was a bit puzzled, 'Is it not painful to walk on?'

'It's excruciatingly painful.'

To which I replied, 'Well, you shouldn't be walking on it, you should have waited till we came in and we could have carried you out.' But she wouldn't have any of this. I could quite understand because as she was hobbling down the path, I could see all the net curtains twitching. She wanted to be seen walking, not carried out. We took her to the casualty and handed a letter from her GP to one of the staff.

10:47 AM

IT WAS NON stop this morning. As soon as we had dropped her we were called to someone having a fit in a shop. This particular shop is on two levels. As we approached the upper level we saw a man waving in panic with both arms. As I got out of the ambulance with my equipment he said, 'Up here, quick.' We made our way up to the shop on the second level, where we found a lady lying on the floor. She had just come out of the fit and was still lying on her side. I'm afraid that wasn't going to stop shoppers coming in and out, they were actually stepping over her. Even as I was kneeling down to find out how she was people were still doing it. One person put her hand on my shoulder so she could step over me and the patient! It must have been some sale! The lady slowly got herself together and told me she was epileptic and could vaguely remember collapsing. I spoke to one of the more caring customers, who told me that after she'd fallen she'd started shaking, then went rigid and turned blue, but quite quickly had come out of her fit. I talked to her gently while I was checking her vital signs, her pulse and her level of consciousness. Even when we got her onto the ambulance I could see she was still suffering from a lack of oxygen in her system since she was still blue around the mouth. So I gave her oxygen which improved her condition by the time we arrived at hospital.

OPPOSITE: *Removing our patient from the shopping centre.*

11:35 AM

AS WE LEFT her at casualty we got another urgent call.
I asked if we could have our meal break but Control said
they were snowed under. 'Would you mind doing this one,
and we'll get you straight back.' We looked at each other,
we'd heard that story before! It was to transfer a seriously ill
child from one hospital to another. We were already at the
RVI, so we just had to drive from the casualty along to the
main entrance and go up to the children's wards to collect
this poor girl, who was unconscious. She was only eight and
had suffered a stroke, which is extremely rare in someone so
young. In the ambulance she was accompanied by her
mother and a children's nurse. We had her lying on her side
and she was non-responsive. Karen talked to the mother and
did her best to reassure her. It must be distressing to see
your little girl just lying there, lost to the world. Before we
took the job we were complaining because we hadn't had a
bite to eat since 7.00 a.m. After seeing her, our whinging seemed a bit pathetic. If we transfer a patient, we usually take
the nurse back to her hospital. We do this most happily,

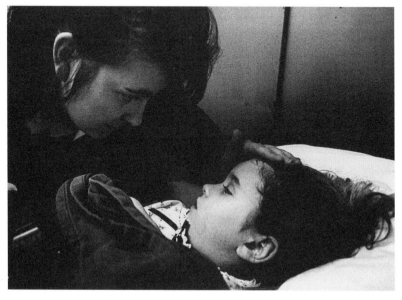

This morning's eight-year-old patient.

the only thing is we point out that she could be still on board for some time if we get called out for an emergency. But of course, sod's law does occasionally work positively. We once had a midwife with us when we were called to an emergency maternity job and another time we were called to a serious head injury and the nurse was a specialist in neurology. This journey back contained no such drama.

12:20 PM

CONTROL TOLD US to return to the station for a meal break. I'd forgotten my sandwiches yet again. Lunch consisted of four cups of coffee. I knew I'd spend much of the afternoon looking for a loo.

13:17 PM

AS SOON AS I got the next call I asked for a police presence. It was a report of an assault at a domestic dispute. When we arrived we were met by five police cars. We all went up to the door, but it turned out to be a hoax call. This was the third or fourth time someone had rung up saying there had been a serious assault and an ambulance was needed at this particular house. It was obviously some kind of vendetta – a neighbourhood dispute.

Hoax calls take time. Even when we know others have been to the place before, we always assume that the call is genuine, we never take chances. Even if we've been there an hour before, we still check it out and give it the same importance as any other job. With this particular job we liaised with the police and cleared at 13.45 p.m. Control told us to return to station.

Real domestics can involve anything from blunt words to sharp knives being thrown. Two years ago we received a call to go to a 'domestic' in a mining village outside Blaydon and, as ever, because they can be volatile affairs we had the police there to support us. The traffic was light so we got to

Karen confirming the details of a hoax call.

the area in about fifteen minutes. But in this village there are no roads between the house only communal gardens and we had to drive down the narrow lane at the back of the houses. We probably had no more than a couple of inches to spare on either side.

I walked ahead doing a recce, but I didn't need to look for the number, I could hear the shouting. The window of the house had been smashed and the curtains were billowing out into the night. The police were already there, trying to calm the man down. He was holding his head, shaking it from side to side, shouting and screaming with pain. To say he was in agony would be an understatement. I've seldom seen anyone in such pain, his whole face was bright red, from what looked like severe scalding. The image I am left with is of a lobster which has just been pulled out of boiling water.

The simple action to take with burns of that degree is to cover with a damp, lint-free cloth such as a non-fluffy tea towel, or if possible use cling film around the affected area to keep out infection, but still leave the injuries visible. You must never do what we sometimes turn up to and find some people have done, and wrap a nice fluffy towel around it, all the fluff sticks to the burnt flesh and causes havoc. We treated him with special burns dressings: lint-free aseptic towels which we soak in a solution of water with 0.9 per cent sodium chloride which has the same alkalinity as blood. As we were doing this the police told us what background information they'd managed to find out.

The couple had been drinking all night long and they were absolutely out of their minds. By midnight they'd become so angry with each other, they'd had a fight and in a fit of rage the wife had stormed out into the kitchen and put on a pressure cooker full of water. Then she came back into the living room and the fighting started again. He got the better of her, so she went back to the kitchen and picked up the pressure cooker which was now boiling. When she came out he was sitting on the settee facing away from the kitchen. She crept up behind him and poured the boiling water over his head. He had been boiled alive, yet even in that state he had managed to punch her and break her nose. She had fled the coup and was nowhere to be seen.

We got him onto the ambulance and took his shirt off. The burns stopped at his neck in a ring that looked as if he'd been out in the sun wearing a t-shirt. We couldn't give him any pain relief because he was so drunk. Nor could we get him to hospital with any speed because we had to negotiate the narrow back lanes, knocking several 'For Sale' boards down in the process. All I could do on the way to hospital was reassure him and keep the face towels wet. He certainly had a few months of treatment ahead of him and I wouldn't like to have put money on the state of his marriage.

14:15 PM

ON THE WAY back to the station we stopped off at a newsagent and I managed to grab a sandwich to eat back at the station. I just had five minutes to sit down and finish it, then the 'phone rang. We had to go to the main police station in Newcastle for someone who was in labour. We didn't

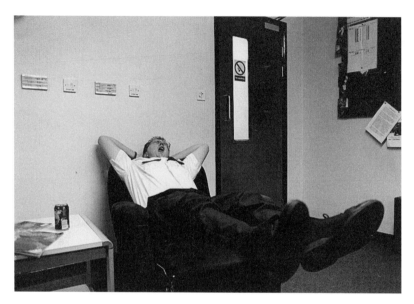

Relaxing at Central.

get any more details. It could have been a prisoner or an officer, but it seemed a strange place to go into labour. Not the ideal location to kick off your life.

At the police station's front desk I asked, 'Somebody in labour?' The policeman said, 'Oh yes, I'll get her for you.' The lady walked through and I sat her down and asked what had been happening. She told me that she'd been shopping, and had started to feel pains. This was her third baby, so she was well experienced in these matters. She thought it was due very soon and had wisely walked to a nearby police station, so that they could contact us, or in an emergency someone in the station could probably have delivered it. The police were relieved to see her safely ushered out.

In the ambulance she explained that her waters hadn't gone, but she was starting to feel contractions coming. It was a fairly routine transfer into hospital. I knew we had quite a few minutes to get her there and told her so. I should never have said it, because someone up there heard, and decided the ambulance would develop a fuel fault, which meant that every few yards it would hiccough and back fire. As it happened we didn't have far to go, and on a wing and a prayer and three cylinders, with the hiccough progressing into a particularly violent form of whooping cough, we limped on. The lady took it all in good spirits, but she was certainly going to have a bonny bouncing baby after that particular ride.

We radioed Control who said they were inundated with work so could we limp back to the station and swop vehicles. On our return we rang the workshops and booked in the ambulance for that evening.

As ambulance men we're taught how to deliver babies but, for some reason or other, it's always tagged onto the back of the course. The first maternity case I got was a real downer. A woman was in labour and needed to get to hospital. When we got to her she was quite far on with her labour and was having contractions every two minutes or less and had the urge to push. The local doctor arrived just after us to take over. Sadly the baby was stillborn. What made matters worse was that it was almost impossible to get the woman out of the house. She was up in the attic which had really steep stairs. We had to put her onto our carrying chair and lift her down. That was a real struggle. She was very distraught and so were we. I must admit that really affected us.

Although delivering babies is part of our job, midwives are really the people to do it. It would be like a midwife driving an ambulance, quite possible but not ideal. We know the obvious things to do to help a mother deliver a baby, but we are by no means experts. We go out on the road never actually having delivered a baby before. Maybe we should spend some time in a maternity unit as part of our training, like we do in A & E and operating theatres, to witness what goes on and help out. I've delivered five or six babies now but compared to a midwife that's nothing, she might crack through that in a day.

Years ago there were more babies delivered at home and in ambulances. People today are more educated as far as having a baby is concerned and, on the whole, they know when to telephone for an ambulance and when not. Of course that's not always the case. When I was working at Blaydon we had a call to a house on the Scotswood Road. It was midday and when we arrived we found a youngish girl. She told us she'd had what felt like contraction pains the night before, and as she was nearly full term, she'd 'phoned her midwife who had said, 'Look pet, you'll be all right. Wait till tomorrow dinner time and phone me then.' The pains did ease off after she 'phoned, but then they came back again. Instead of telephoning the midwife back right away to say her pains were getting worse she decided that as she'd been told to wait till midday, she would wait till midday.

It was obvious we weren't going to get her to the hospital, the baby was well on it's way. What we did then was panic and start to pray. Neither of us had delivered a baby before. We informed our control of what was happening and in very high squeaky voices we requested a midwife to be sent as quickly as possible.

We carry a basic maternity pack on the ambulance which contains sheets, a dish and clamps for the cord, different pads and dressings – everything we could possibly want or need except instructions on how to deliver a baby! I've often thought that they should include a big illustrated instruction chart in the pack which your mate could discreetly pin up behind the mother-to-be. With total confidence you could then say to her, smile on your face, 'Right now, here we go. No problems.' Luckily in this case it wasn't difficult. She did all the work and delivered a fine baby boy right there in her home. As soon as he was born and everything was OK, and I'd wiped the sweat off my forehead, in came the midwife! We took mother and baby to hospital and I don't mind admitting I think I felt prouder than the father. It was a great feeling.

When it does happen we don't usually have to do much. We send the father off to boil pans of water, telling him to put them on a low heat and watch them until they boil. That gets him out of the way. We make the lady comfortable and quite honestly she delivers the baby, we're often just there to stop it bouncing onto the floor. I was with my mate, Bill, in Dunston once when he literally caught the baby. The mother was on all fours, and pushing hard when the baby shot out and my mate Bill performed a marvellous dive and caught it like a wicket keeper. It was brilliant.

Sometimes when you get a call to deliver someone to a maternity unit you think it's going to be a gentle taxi service job but it gets a bit more exciting. I thought I was going to be in real trouble recently. We picked up a woman from Highfield. She was booked in at a maternity hospital in Newcastle, which was a good half-an-hour's journey. She was having her contractions in the ambulance. So we made her comfortable and to deflect her mind off the pain I said, 'Have you got the hardest bit done?' She looked puzzled so I said, 'You know, the baby's name.'

'Oh no,' she said. 'In any case I need two names.'

'Why two names?'

'I'm having twins.'

I said, 'You're joking, you're having me on here,' and she said, 'No, I'm having twins and there's a problem, they're upside down in the womb and they're going to be born breach.' (That's feet first, which in a single birth is bad enough, but breach twins didn't bear thinking about.) I just said to my mate, very firmly, 'PUT YOUR FOOT DOWN. NOW!' and then said to the girl, 'Don't just sit there, cross your legs.' She laughed so much at our reactions that I was convinced she was going to start giving birth, but luckily we didn't need to break out the maternity pack and got her to the hospital in time.

Of course we hear of some very odd births. I remember one of our lads telling me how he'd arrived a bit late for one. He was told that the woman was giving birth in the toilet at that moment. When they rushed upstairs they found the woman squatting over the loo and the little chap was in the process of being delivered into the pan. Amazingly, he was perfectly all right.

We had another case where a fourteen-year-old girl at school hid the fact that she was pregnant and gave birth in her tights during a lesson. They had to cut her tights off to get the baby out but it too was fine.

One of the oddest cases I had was a call to a lady who was having her eighth or ninth child. The council had knocked two houses into one and the third house was on its way. They were almost kicking the neighbours out to spread this family along the terrace. We thought of suggesting they got the street named after them, because they were about the only people who lived there!

Her contractions were coming every two or three minutes. I'd asked how the previous pregnancies had gone and she reckoned from past experience she was at least an hour away from giving birth. She was far more of an expert than us, so we took things swiftly but didn't rush. We got her into our chair and took her out to the ambulance. She looked so young and innocent, I couldn't believe she'd given birth to so many kids, you'd think butter wouldn't melt in her mouth.

As we carried her out one of us hit a bump which threw the chair about. I can tell you that butter melted very quickly in her mouth because we got expletives from her I'd never even heard before. And she was wrong when she implied that our mothers weren't married. She had been perfectly polite in the house but now she was swearing like a trooper. I couldn't believe it, I was quite taken aback. Once we got her into the ambulance her language deteriorated until she was effing and blinding with every contraction. Her husband, a big chap with tattoos on his arms just sat there letting it all wash over him.

We were about twenty minutes' drive from the hospital when she cried out, 'I can feel it coming, it's on its way.' I thought, oh no. I knew I'd have to take a look, but I thought that if she was like this her old man was not going to be the type to take kindly to me examining his missus. But there was nothing for it, so I said, 'Well, I'm going to have to take a look.' Would you believe she had to ask her husband whether I could or not. To my surprise he wasn't in the slightest bit bothered and just said, 'Right, go on son, have a look, do what you want, get stuck in!' It was night-time and we were out in the country, so we pulled over to the side of the road. The problem with the back of the ambulance is there's not much room. It's much easier if somebody gives birth in a house or in a hospital, but in an ambulance, the bed is only a couple of feet wide and the lights aren't very good. We'd only just pulled over when she issued a long stream of invectives, gave birth, and didn't swear again!

By the time my wife Claire was giving birth I'd been involved in quite a few deliveries. Though most dads like to watch the birth, this dad tried to get in on the action! I wanted to get my hands there at the business end, but the doctor fought me off, much to Claire's relief!

Most of our jobs tend to be either dealing with people who are very ill, even dying. We don't get many jobs where we go along and we actually bring life into the world. To be honest out of choice I'd rather not get involved in other people's births, but when you do get one and everything works well there's nothing better, it's brilliant.

15:00 PM

WE GAVE THE new vehicle a full check and rang Control to say we were available. We were given another technically straightforward transfer of a twenty-year-old from his home to hospital. It was a routine job, but then much of our day is routine, except that when we parked outside his house to pick him up our help was sought by a neighbour. Our impromptu patient must have been twenty stones, had the biggest belly I'd seen all week, was hairy and running down the road on all fours squealing. Unfortunately there's nothing in our training about recapturing Vietnamese pot bellied pigs which have escaped from a city farm! Our human patient looked on patiently as we rounded her up nervously.

I'd never had to round one up before, but I have ended up feeding some pot bellied pigs on a previous case. Three years ago we turned up at a farm to find the yard empty, the farmer dead, and the pigs very hungry. But that's another story!

One of the most surprising animal encounters I've had was when we met ten horses galloping towards us down the A1. They'd obviously escaped and were going to be a danger to traffic. Well, we'd handled pigs and cows but horses are another thing. Our Wild West skills proved a bit shaky.

Eventually the boys in blue arrived and we set off on foot together to try and recapture them. Some of the horses had ropes hanging from their halters so we thought if we could stop one or two, the rest might settle down. However seeing a herd of fluorescent jackets heading for them they panicked and started to gallop and I didn't fancy being pulled along a concrete road playing Wyatt Earp again. My mate came up with a stunning idea. He reckoned they were all mares, so he'd go and find a stallion so they would all follow him. I explained, quietly, that it would probably work the other way round! Then the police came up with an even better idea, they would call in the dog division! Quite how or why the dog handler's experience would rate above ours wasn't discussed. We simply retired to rewrite our instruction book with a chapter on how to handle stray horses. The RSPCA took great pleasure in sorting out the situation for the emergency services.

15:43 PM

A NOTHER URGENT CALL to a doctor's surgery, to take a patient with severe stomach pains to casualty. What no one mentioned was that these pains were making her vomit extensively. She was vomiting because she was completely drunk, in fact she was a right Friday night job and to make matters worse she also smelt. With a projectile vomiting case, you have a nightmare come true. You draw lots for who goes in the back of the ambulance. I could see why the doctor wanted to get rid of her. I drew the short straw, so Karen spent the journey smiling to herself in the front. I tried to settle the lady down and got several bowls ready. She filled them as fast as I held them up. So there I was surrounded by these bowls of vomit and every time Karen had to break suddenly, the contents would fly all over the place. It finished up in my shoes, on my trousers, all over the ambulance. It was a mess. We are talking serious driving

OPPOSITE: An unexpected pot-bellied patient.

here trying to get shot of her. But it was a 'Catch-22' situation. The faster we drove the more she puked up, the slower Karen drove, the longer she was with me. As soon as we got her into the hospital it was out with the mop and the air fresheners.

During the summer of the Tall Ships' visit to Newcastle, we received a call to a restaurant down by the quayside to an old lady with intense abdominal pain. When we got there she didn't look too good. Her husband told us that for a treat they'd come out to look at the ships and then have lunch. They had both ordered fish and chips and mushy peas. The old boy didn't feel like eating so rather than waste it, the old lady had eaten his as well. Not surprisingly, she had then begun to feel unwell which was when we got the 'phone call. We got her into the back of the ambulance, laid her down and strapped her in. I was sitting opposite talking to her when she suddenly said, 'I feel sick,' and then puked up right in my lap. I tell you there were bits of fish, chewed up chips, peas and carrots all over me. I was covered. When I reached for my handkerchief, it was even in my pockets. Because it was a hot day the back of the ambulance was sweltering. With the stink and the humidity I had to sit next to the air vent. When we got to the hospital I looked more unwell than she did, I was almost green. The ambulance smelt like a fishmonger's for the rest of the week. It was terrible.

17:05 PM

WE GOT A call to a person in a diabetic coma at the east end of Newcastle and when we arrived in the street, it was a dead end, but outside the last house there was a lady waving to us. We grabbed our equipment and were shown into a downstairs flat and into the bathroom where there was a man lying face down. The first thing I did was ask his wife about his history. She said he was a diabetic and that he had had a hypoglycaemic attack before, where his blood sugar level had fallen so low that he had become unconscious. He had been poorly for some time and had been vomiting a lot. He'd missed a couple of meals and that was why he had become hypoglycaemic. As I checked him he was sweating and had a very rapid pulse. I tried asking him how he was, but he was right out of it.

In a case like this we give a drug called Glucogen, which as it's name suggests increases the glucose in the blood. We have to mix this drug ourselves. The two components are carried in separate containers in a plastic case. There is liquid in one and powder in the other. You pierce the rubber top of one container and draw up the fluid with a syringe. This is added to the powder and shaken to mix it. Then using the same syringe you draw the mixture up and give 1 mg intramuscularly. The drug takes effect quickly, and within five minutes this chap had reverted to full consciousness. It's a magic potion. When he was able to talk I gave him some chocolate to provide carbohydrates. By the time we got him to hospital he wanted us to turn round and go back, he'd totally recovered. A satisfying result for him and us.

When a paramedic gives any drug there's a great deal of paperwork to fill in. We were told we could go back to the station to complete this and also sign the drug record books and replace the Glucogen. It took us twenty minutes to complete the paperwork and we kept looking up at the clock wondering if we'd get another job in the last forty minutes of our shift.

Whatever shift you're working on you always hope that the last job of the day will be simple. We were working a four-to-midnight shift a while back and had just dropped someone off at the hospital and radioed in that we were clear. It was 11.50 p.m. so Control told us to return to the station. My mate Peter was pleased because he wanted to get away sharply at midnight. We were on our way back and just beginning to relax when the radio cracked into life. 'Blaydon 312 emergency call.' Our hearts sank. Control apologized saying that we were the nearest vehicle. Apparently it was a drugs overdose and we'd be met by the police. In fact it was just round the corner from where we were so Pete was really pleased because with any luck it would be a quick job.

The time-consuming part of overdose calls is usually persuading them to come in the ambulance with us. Once they're in there's not much we can do except head for casualty. We had expected to see the police when we arrived but all we saw were these lads about seventeen or eighteen years old who were either drunk or high on drugs. One of them was lying down thrashing around and bashing his forehead on the ground. The first thing we had to do was protect his head. I clasped my hands and got hold of his head so that he wouldn't cause himself any more damage. Then his arms and legs started thrashing around and he gave me a hard punch right on the cheek. This was not going to be a quick one.

I shouted for someone to get hold of his arms to restrain him. At that moment the police arrived in a panda car and four burly lads got out. They soon got hold of him and together we dumped him unceremoniously onto the stretcher. We then had the problem of getting him into the ambulance where there isn't room for four people to hold a patient down on the stretcher. One of the police came up with a good idea. They handcuffed each wrist to the main substructure of the bed. We then strapped his legs down. He was restrained but still fighting, well out of control. With the combination of drugs and drink he was like man mountain, incredibly strong, and potentially dangerous once we arrived at the hospital. They said they'd let one of the policemen come with us to help, the rest were off to another job.

By the time we got to the hospital the lad had calmed down. We gave the doctor the full story, and between us decided he'd be all right to untie and move onto a hospital bed, leaving the policeman to stand guard. We undid the straps around his legs and waited for the policeman to unlock the two sets of handcuffs which anchored the lad to our bed. The policeman looked slightly embarrassed as he searched his pockets. Peter looked at him as if to say 'very funny', then realized he wasn't joking. We had to wait over an hour and a half before the police were able to send another man with a set of keys. That really pleased Pete.

18:21 PM

THE RED 'PHONE rang. It was a 999 call to a home at the north end of town, a possible suicide attempt. When we got there we found this middle-aged chap who suffered from epilepsy. He was drunk and certainly suicidal. His poor wife was beside herself, crying and very distressed. She said he'd threatened to take his life with an overdose of tablets. She was so desperate, but hadn't known who to telephone and had finally chosen the ambulance service. Technically this was not a difficult job, because medically there was nothing we could do. It was really a question of gaining their confidence and persuading him to go to hospital with us where the staff would help him. He was not convinced and refused to go with us. There are many cases where you turn up and the patient refuses to go with you. All you do is get them to sign the book and leave, but I knew we couldn't leave this man in the house, something had to be done with him. When we told his wife that we'd keep trying there was a tremendous sense of relief, she couldn't thank us enough.

From our point of view this is where our problems start. We can't force a person who has swallowed tablets to go to hospital. They are within their rights to refuse. So at first you reason with them, and gently persuade. If that gets nowhere you have to start being truthful. If they've taken a lot of tablets I explain quite firmly that we can leave them but they'll be taken out tomorrow, not by us but by an undertaker. This blunt approach usually triggers some last contact with reality and they go with you. If they still won't come, I 'phone the police. Then in the ambulance it's a case of tender loving care (TLC) until we get to the hospital.

This evening's patient saw sense and came along. His wife accompanied us to the hospital where I had a word with the medical staff. Hopefully they'd be able to look into more long-term help for the family.

There are so many suicide attempts every Friday night that the Samaritans provide a counselling service in the main

OVERLEAF: *En route to an emergency.*

Newcastle casualty department. I'm not sure exactly what it says about society, but I'm sure it isn't a healthy sign. Most suicides are attempted at night, and though the vast majority are half-hearted and unsuccessful, more like cries for help, when someone does succeed they tend to do so in a spectacular fashion.

I was working at one of our rural stations when we got a call one evening, just before midnight, to a railway station. Control told us that a train driver had dialled 999 because he'd hit something on the line. We turned up at the railway station at exactly the same time as the British Rail police. There was a goods train in the station and another just pulling in from the other direction. We found our driver sitting in the cab of the first train. He was obviously very shaken. He said he hadn't known if he'd hit a person, an animal or just a cardboard box until he pulled up at the next station, he looked underneath and found flesh hanging from the chassis. He reckoned the hit had happened a couple of miles back up the track from the station. We decided my mate would go with two of the police on the other train and travel back up the line slowly. I would drive the ambulance to the next station further down the line and approach from the opposite direction.

As I walked into the station I was met by a British Rail bloke, some chief gaffer type, and we began to move along the line. By now it was after one o'clock. It was a very still night with a full moon so it was quite light with strong shadows. Most of the line ran through open countryside, but at one point we had to walk round the back of a derelict factory. It was dead quiet, except that every now and then there would be a clanging sound, which made me feel a bit uneasy. But the most unnerving part of the walk came when we had to pass a long, stationary goods train carrying large oil tankers. Normally, when you walk past a train at a station you're up at platform level, but we were down on the embankment at wheel height with the large dark cylinders looming above us. As we moved away from the engine and the low thud became quieter, you could hear occasional clicking sounds coming from the tanks. We kept on walking in single file without saying a word to each other. The tanks seemed menacing as they cast strange shadows along the line. The whole thing was absolutely eerie. Then there was silence, like a world that's stopped. If anybody had come out from the shadows and clapped we'd all have been off like a shot. About three hundred yards past the train we saw the others. They'd found the remains of a human being. The entrails were spread over fifty yards, the backbone was lying on its own, all in all a bit of a mess.

The trouble with our body bags is that they're thin plastic and from experience we know that the sharp bits of bodies rip them. So when you lift the bag everything falls out. The British Rail police had obviously done this job a good few times before as well, because they produced carrier bags from their pockets. We had to collect whatever we could. It was a rum job but somebody has got to pick up the bits. If we didn't do it, the police would have to, if they didn't it would be down to the undertaker. And, being out in the country, if we'd left it that long the foxes would have done the job for us all.

My mate had arrived before me and was picking up the feet and legs and I went along towards him picking up the arms and hands. There were enough clues to tell that it had been a man once. All the time we were liaising over the portable radios, reporting what we'd found. Somewhere in the middle we discovered the head. That was pretty disturbing. The eyes were gone.

By now it was about three o'clock. One of the policemen nodded towards some distant car headlights. 'Here they come!' The ghouls were arriving.

These are the people who own radio scanners and keep them tuned across the emergency frequencies, listening out for something juicy. They must have thought that Christmas had come early that night. Throughout the search we'd been in radio contact with our Control, keeping them updated, in case we needed help and so they had some idea of how long we'd be tied up. To the eavesdroppers this was better than if we'd sent personal telegrams inviting them along and put up neon signs to show them the way. There are some very sad people out there. After the first car had cruised past, others followed. Word doesn't seem to take long to spread between these like-minded individuals. There must have been seven or eight vehicles in the end. The police said there was nothing they could do to stop them, as long as they were just driving around quite legally.

After we'd picked up the bits of his body we found the man's clothes. They were down the embankment, all carefully folded and he'd placed his shoes alongside them. When the police looked for identification they found that he'd written several letters and had left them in his neatly folded jacket. There were also two empty cans of beer. It was a pretty well organized preparation for death.

We didn't put the bags with the remains on a stretcher, just laid them on the floor. When we got to the mortuary blood was dripping out of the ambulance. The mortuary attendant told us to put the bags on a slab, and as we did one of them tore and a hand dropped out. It was a horror story. But if you decide to jump in front of a train that's doing 70–80 mph you're going to get ripped apart. There is no point in pretending anything else.

I can't help but feel sympathetic towards someone who obviously meant business like he did. I can see how family problems or pressures at work, or equally the stress of not having work, can build up. But it's a desperate person who does something like that bloke did that night in such a calculating way.

One of the first suicide attempts I was called to was particularly sad. He was a paraplegic who was into religion in a big way. He'd been disabled jumping off a bridge in an attempt to get nearer to God. By all accounts he'd got pretty close to meeting him, but not near enough. He then decided to kill himself by rolling his wheelchair in front of a train coming into a station. He'd parked his chair up on the far end of the platform and when he'd seen the train approaching he'd pushed himself down the platform as fast as he could towards it. Then, as the train got closer, he pulled the brake on one wheel which turned the wheelchair towards the track. A couple more quick thrusts on the wheels

Karen receiving an emergency call.

and he was off the platform. The train hit him in mid-air and he was thrown back onto the platform and literally wrapped around a lamp post. He broke his leg and was bleeding internally, but essentially he was not too badly injured, which was a really big disappointment to him. He'd desperately wanted to die.

Most suicide attempts are less dramatic, even less successful, and usually involve a drugs overdose. You name the drug and we've picked up people who've taken it. We've been called to everyone from a mother with a baby and four toddlers, to a wealthy businessman, even a few little old grannies. Sometimes you can see straight away the pressures the patient is under as soon as you arrive at the call. There was one recently where I can remember the whole scene. I can picture the house. When we turned up the family had already dragged the old granny outside. We met her on the path but couldn't get too much of a history from her immediately. The garden is not the place to stand and ask people what the problem is, so we got her onto the ambulance. She said she'd just taken the tablets, a whole whack of them, because the family was falling apart and it was all her fault. Then the rest of the family decided they wanted to go to hospital with her. We've only got four seats, but there were about ten of them, so there was a heated discussion about who should go! All the old tensions came out and they continued to come out as we bounced along in the ambulance. While they were arguing, I sat and tried to get as much history as I could from the old lady and at the same time act as peacemaker to this warring family! I was trying to get her to tell me how many tablets she'd taken and what type they were. But of course everyone else knew better than her: 'She took twenty half an hour ago.' Then, 'Take no notice, she's took them ten minutes ago.' There are always so many different accounts on these occasions that we like to get into the house to judge for ourselves what the person might have taken. If you can see the bottle you can identify the tablets and work out from the date the pills were dispensed roughly how many might have been left.

What we did gather was that she'd locked herself in the toilet and taken a bottle of tablets. Of course when the family had realized what had happened the balloon went up, and the poor old dear was in trouble again for doing it, which made her feel even worse. In the end we were pretty sure that what she'd taken were harmless enough.

There are a lot of dodgy tablets around, each with a different effect on the body. Paracetamol is a classic. The attempters knock back the contents of a bottle and then wait to feel sleepy or ill. But of course that drug doesn't work that way. Paracetamol attacks the kidneys and liver in the longer term and then you're done for. So often the difficulty for us is to persuade someone who's made their grand gesture and now feels a bit stupid, but perfectly well, that if they don't come with us at once they'll be dead by the morning. Other drugs have completely different effects, which is why it's important to find out just what tablets they have taken.

Whatever they've taken our job is to speed them to hospital where the treatment is given. The common treatment is to give a flavoured drink which immediately causes the patient to puke up the contents of the stomach. There will be time for counselling later. If they're lucky. Out of the hundreds of people I've taken to hospital who have taken an overdose, I only know of one person who has actually died. She was a disabled woman, living with her husband who was immobilized after a stroke. I don't know what led up to it. When we got there, she was well dead. We tried to resuscitate her but we were too late. The doctor was called and she certified her dead. The lady had gone into the bathroom and taken a cocktail of pills, and it had worked. I felt really sorry for the old boy who was in a wheelchair, totally helpless. Because of his stroke, he couldn't even communicate, all he could do was sit there and cry, it was heartbreaking.

Another suicide method which has a high success rate in my experience is to use a gun. One morning Control passed us an emergency call with no details except the address. A woman had phoned 999 in an absolute panic, given an address and put the 'phone down before they could get any more information. It took us about fifteen minutes to get to the area and find the road. As Sod's law would have it, of course, it was a house name, not a number. All the houses were on one side, with farm land on the other. So we had to drive slowly along the wrong side of the road looking for the house name. Then we saw a woman waving. As we pulled up we could hear her shouting 'Quick, quick, hurry, hurry.' I moved as fast as I could without running, but at a brisk pace to keep up with the woman.

She led the way into the house and shouted, 'He's upstairs.' I started to climb, but halfway up stopped, turned and asked, 'What exactly is the problem?' She said, 'He's got a gun.' So I quickly decided not to go any further! My first thought was to go outside into the front garden to warn my mate and get her to radio for police help, but then I realized the man would have had a perfect field of vision to take a clear pot shot at me. So I stood underneath the porch and shouted to Bernie, my mate, 'Get the police, he's got a gun.' I stood there waiting for her to radio, but Sod's law again, we were in a blind spot and she couldn't raise Control. While Bernie was trying to get through I tried to calm the woman down and find out what had happened.

'He's got a gun has he?'

'Yes,' she said, 'I heard it go off. He keeps guns.' I kept one eye on her and the other on the stairs.

'I got up to make breakfast and when I came downstairs I heard the gun go off. I rushed upstairs and he was lying completely still on the bed with a gun on top of him.' This woman was crying and screaming and I kept saying, 'Now, calm down.' But through all of this, bit by bit, I ascertained that she was convinced that he was dead. Despite this she still screamed, 'You've got to do something, you've got to help me.'

With no sign of any back up I told her to wait downstairs while I went up. I was bloody wary as I climbed the stairs. If a floorboard had squeaked, I'd have been off. All the time I was thinking, what if he's taken a shot at himself but it was only a glancing blow. If he's still alive he could take a pot shot at the next person who comes through the door. Yet I also thought that he could still be alive and needing my help. Rightly or wrongly at the time, I thought if he wants my help, I'm going to have to give it.

The bedroom door was open a couple of inches. I moved across the landing but all I could see through the gap was a wall. I guessed that the bed would be behind the door so I stood as far as I could to one side, kicked the door open and jumped back. I thought if he's going to take a shot he'll do it now, but nothing happened. Then I looked through the crack between the door and the door frame and could see him lying motionless on the bed. My heart was beating like mad as I went into the room, but all fear disappeared when I got close to him. He was lying on his side on top of the bed wearing his pyjamas. As I felt for a pulse I could see there was little point. There was a small entrance hole, a huge exit wound and a lot of his brain on the bed. He was very obviously dead. The rifle he'd used was beside him.

I heard several distant sirens. The Seventh Cavalry were arriving, a bit late mind you, but they were on their way. Once they'd known an ambulance was calling for assistance they'd put their foot down. Apart from feeling for a pulse I didn't touch the man. As soon as the police arrived we handed everything over to them. It was a small village and the local doctor soon came to certify him dead and stood us down. The strange thing was that while all this had been going on across the landing his thirteen-year-old son was asleep in his bedroom with his labrador.

Of course not everyone succeeds in killing themselves. We were called out to one patient who'd obviously meant business. The only description we were given was of an attempted suicide by a young lad. It wasn't until we got there that we established what had happened.

We had to weave our way through a big housing estate. First we couldn't find the street, then having found the street, we couldn't find the number. When we did get there the door was open, which is always an ominous sign, especially when you can hear the family inside screaming and shouting. As we went in one of them pushed us upstairs saying, 'He's hung himself.' Upstairs on the landing we could see an open loft hatch with a rope dangling through it. I thought we'd have to climb up into the roof to find the lad, but they pushed us on into one of the bedrooms. The lad was lying on the floor in agony. He hadn't killed himself but had managed to give himself a terrible rope burn. Where the noose had been tight around his neck, all the skin was torn off. It must have been very painful. As I dressed the raw flesh he told me that he'd climbed up into the loft, tied one end of the rope around a beam, knotted the other end around his neck and jumped out through the loft hatch. Luckily for him the knot had slipped, but not before it had torn the skin away from under his chin. We took him to hospital, but before the doctor could see him the idiot discharged himself.

The least successful method tends to be slashed wrists which is very inefficient, but often very messy. Where young blokes are concerned there's always a girl involved somewhere, and vice versa. One case in particular comes to mind because, in all my life, it was the most painful injury I've ever seen anybody deliberately inflict on themselves.

The call was to a camping site at a local beauty spot.

When we pulled up we found a lad with a broken hand and the most awful slashes to his wrists. He was in an amazingly bad way, just screaming and shouting in agony. There was another lad and two girls with him who were obviously concerned for him, but he was having nothing to do with them. We couldn't give him any pain-killing gas because we could smell that he'd had a fair bit to drink. We dressed the wrists to stop the blood and said we'd take him to hospital. When we were about to set off we asked if any of the others would come with us but he said he didn't want them to. As we drove to the hospital he told me what had happened.

He'd gone camping for the weekend with his girlfriend and another couple. They were young kids, all about eighteen years old, and it was the first time they'd been away camping together. They'd taken two tents and expected to be in for a fun weekend. Many drinks later our lad's girlfriend had fallen for the other boy. The other girl had so much to drink that she wasn't at all bothered and the new couple ended up in a tent together. This left our boy without his girlfriend who, he told us, he loved. The combination of circumstances and alcohol had made him really cheesed off. So he decided to try and end it all. He got an empty baked bean tin, pressed the centre inwards and waggled the two ends until he managed to separate the top from the bottom. This left two halves with sharp edges, ideal for hacking away at his arms. He did a pretty good job of ripping up his flesh, but that wasn't enough so he decided to put his fist through the toughened glass of his own car window.

I thought what a fool, what a bloody idiot he'd been. He should have said, 'Be my girl or I'm going to leave you here.' After all it was his car so he could have just driven off and made them get the bus back home or worse still walk. That really would have screwed them up. It's what I would have done. But of course in the ambulance you've got to be tactful even if someone has done something stupid, so I just reassured him, bandaged him up, and forced myself to say nothing.

On another occasion we were called to a high rise block. As usual the call came through at 6.55 a.m. Why does five

An emergency call to a block of flats.

minutes before the end of our twelve-hour shifts seem to be such a low point in so many people's lives?

The call simply said that someone had overdosed in a flat up on the ninth floor of a Gateshead tower block. We asked for the police to be informed as the flats are in a rough area and sometimes people who've had a go at themselves can become violent towards us when we try to stop them becoming a statistic. We got out of the lift which smelt like a public loo and into the dark corridor which was no better. Unfortunately we'd arrived first. The lift doors closed and the lift clattered off to another floor. It was very quiet, and there were no obvious signs of any problems. We knocked on the door but there was no answer, so I knocked again a bit harder. The door was flung open and there was this thin bloke standing there, covered in blood pointing a bread knife at me. He lunged at me but I managed to dodge out of the way. He was obviously drunk, out of his mind and in a complete rage. We knew that there were only two ways out. The first was by the lift which had disappeared and I wasn't in the mood to press the call button and stand around making small talk. The only other route was the fire escape which was behind the man with the knife. Out of the corner of my eye I saw that my mate was about to swing our steel carrying chair at the bloke and for some reason I went into motor mouth overdrive. If what I said took *him* by surprise, it certainly surprised me. 'Please give me the knife, I need it.' He paused. 'Look, I need your knife. I've got to have it.' He just stood there, mouth open, bewildered. I moved forward, grabbed it and pointed it at him. He had to do the talking then. I couldn't have done anything else. I certainly wasn't going to hand it back to him or put it back in his kitchen drawer.

I calmed him down and persuaded him to go back into the flat and let us take a look at his wounds, and he started to talk. He was such a sad case. He'd been diagnosed HIV positive. His family had said that they didn't want to know him anymore and had abandoned him. It had all got too much and he'd decided to take alcohol, a drug overdose and then use a bread knife to try to saw his arm off at the elbow. We managed to stop the blood, bandage him up and calm him down before the police arrived in great numbers. It's always sod's law that just as you've got your violent patient calm and happy, ten policemen will suddenly turn up and make him agitated again. But we took him down to the ambulance and off to hospital.

Of course anyone who is diagnosed as HIV positive would receive counselling. But I can quite understand that in those darkest moments when you're sitting alone in a dingy flat and you've had a few beers, it would all become too much. We found out some time later that he'd died of AIDS.

In an exception to the five-minutes-before-the-end-of-shift rule we got a call from Control one Friday morning to say that a woman had found her husband locked in the garage with the car engine running. Within four minutes of the call we were there. We were met on the drive of a posh house by a smartly dressed woman in her fifties in a state of high anxiety. Her husband had locked the up and over garage door and hidden both sets of keys. The only other way in was through the door leading from the house. She showed us through the kitchen to the utility room which was also locked. We managed to force it open a few inches but the husband had been clever enough to park the car right up against the door.

We could hear the engine, and as soon as we'd got a gap in the door you could smell the fumes. My mate Steve kicked the top of the door in and we managed to make a gap big enough to scrabble our way in. The car was brand new and without thinking I shouted to the woman to ask if she'd mind us climbing on it. She was bewildered, the last thing she expected was concern about her car. She said, 'Yes, yes, just climb in, get him out.' I stood on the bonnet which made these awful metallic crumpling noises as I walked across it, all ten and a half stones of me. I jumped across the bonnet and tried the driver's door but it was locked. I could clearly see the bloke in the car, slumped in the driver's seat not looking at all well. The window was open a bit on the driver's side, but not enough to get my hand in. He'd obviously thought things through because he'd wound down the passenger window both at the rear and the front to let the gases in. But there was no way we could get in because he'd parked the car carefully so that the doors were tight against the wall. All the time we were trying to get at him the fumes were getting worse.

Then Steve got onto the roof, which promptly caved in. This gave him more room to squirm inside the car via the passenger window. While Steve was trying to get into the car to turn off the engine, I tried to get the garage door open. The fumes were really, really bad by now. Once inside Steve switched off the engine, and while he looked after the husband I tried desperately to get the garage doors open. There were two steel bars running horizontally from the centre which locked the door closed. I just bent the bars back and pushed the door open. What a relief when the fresh air hit us.

In any life-threatening situation you either take the patient away from the danger or the danger away from the patient. We knew we had to take the patient and us away from the danger. However our redesign of the car meant that the front doors wouldn't open, so the quickest means was to move the man and the car. With the man still in the driver's seat and Steve steering, not very well, from the passenger's seat, I pushed the car out.

With the adrenaline pumping you find you're stronger than you think. While I pushed I could hear a terrible scraping sound as the passenger door caught the garage door frame and wrenched off the wing mirror. We finished with one wheel in the flower bed and, being a bit of a car lover, all I could think of was this couple's lovely new vehicle which we were quickly wrecking.

What we didn't know was how long he'd been in the garage. It could have been four minutes, it might have been forty. However long he'd been in there he'd been lucky. Steve had established that he was still breathing and that he had a pulse. But he was pink, a textbook example of carbon monoxide poisoning. By now of course, all the neighbours had started to arrive. Once they see those blue ambulance lights they're out of their houses wanting to know what's going on.

The chap was unconscious, out for the count, but he was lucky, there was a fair chance that he'd be all right. We got him onto the bed in the ambulance and gave him oxygen, monitoring his vital signs very closely as we raced to hospital. I spoke to his wife while we were on the way. We don't pry, but just try to glean any information which might help the hospital have an overview of the situation. He had no family problems, no mortgage, no debts and was due to retire in a couple of years from a firm where he'd worked for nearly forty years. The day before he'd been told at work, 'Don't come back on Monday, you're surplus to requirement.' He had lived for his job and he couldn't come to terms with the idea of being made redundant. In the space of those few minutes his whole world had disintegrated and he couldn't hack it. He didn't go in on the following day, but locked himself in the garage where his wife had found him. She was as stunned by the fact that she hadn't realized how badly her husband had taken it all, as she was about what he'd actually done. She'd obviously known he was unhappy but she never dreamt he would try and take his life. We often pass the house and I've no idea how he is. But I still rib Steve about his reversing!

I was in the middle of eating my fish and chips one night when we got a call. A man who had been out walking with his dog had spotted a bottle of whisky on the wall of a viaduct which crossed a disused railway line. Something made him look over the side and there, a hundred feet or more below, was a body. It was such a long way down that the bloke hadn't tried to go and see what had happened, but had run for the 'phone and called for the ambulance.

There are three viaducts around that area, but we'd been given the local name so we knew which one it was. As we pulled up at the start of the viaduct the heavens opened. We looked over the top of the six-foot-high wall and sure enough there was a body lying at the bottom. We decided there were two possibilities: the person had either been walking along down on the disused railway line and collapsed, or had fallen off the viaduct. If it was the latter he'd be a goner. Now I had the classic dilemma of what to take with me. There was no way we could get the stretcher down the steep embankment, and frankly I thought that if he *had* fallen the hundred feet there'd be no great hurry. If, on the other hand, he'd had a heart attack we'd need a completely different set of gear. So I took the portable hand radio with me so I could liaise with my mate and scrambled down the wet, slippery slope.

The man, who must have been in his seventies, was lying with his back against a tree, and as I approached I could tell he was conscious. As I got closer I asked, 'You all right then?' He mumbled that his hand hurt. He sounded as though he'd had a bit to drink. I carried out a quick examination of the rest of his body and although he was having some problems breathing the only real problem I could find with his hand was a broken finger. I asked if he could remember what had happened.

'I was having a drink of whisky when I fell off the bridge, didn't I.' The empty bottle up on the wall reinforced his story. He said he remembered hitting the branches of a large tree which had broken his fall, and then he'd hit smaller trees before landing in the marshy valley bottom, to the side of the old track below the viaduct.

We were then faced with the task of getting him out. He was so drunk there was no way he'd have been able to walk, and his breathing difficulties meant that we'd have to carry him in a sitting position, up the steep banks, which were on either side. We're talking vertical faces here which made the north face of the Eiger look like a slight incline.

We carry three types of stretcher on our ambulances: the bed on wheels which you can sit or lie a patient on, an orthopaedic stretcher, and a paraguard. The paraguard is a rescue stretcher which you strap the patient to so you can manhandle it, and it would have been perfect for him if he'd not had breathing problems. We had no choice but to use our carrying chair to keep him upright. But the boggy ground and the steep slope weren't the easiest of conditions to use it in. So we decided to call for the boys with the blue lights, big red engines and yellow hats. They rigged up some ropes and in the end four of us took hold of a corner each and with somebody pushing us as well we somehow managed to get the old boy up the side of the bank. He sat in the chair happily inebriated throughout. He didn't, or couldn't, say much on the way to hospital, but from the odd comment about particular hospital wards he'd been on before my thinking was that he had chest cancer and was trying to top himself.

He'd had a one in a million chance of surviving such a fall, it was sheer fluke. It was summertime and even if we hadn't arrived he would probably have sobered up and walked off eventually. In winter he'd have been a gonner from hypothermia. I'll never really know if he fell or jumped but I often think of him sitting there with his back to the tree.

19:15 PM

WE RADIOED BACK to Control that we were clear and we were told to stand down. It had been a long day and we were keen to get back to the station and get home. But of course when we got back we had all the paperwork to do. Every patient we pick up has to be logged, all our mileages for every patient have to be recorded and a record of whether they were emergency or urgent calls or just patients being transferred. We then have to replace any equipment that we've used during the day such as oxygen masks or bandages and remove the paramedic drugs case, fill in the register, then lock it away. The vehicle then has to be fuelled up and quite often at the end of the day there's a queue of other ambulances. We eventually left tonight at 19.50, having arrived in the morning at 06.30. Another long day over.

— DAY —

FOUR

06:30 AM

IARRIVED AT CENTRAL at 6.30 a.m. this morning to find we had been issued with one of Northumbria Ambulance Service's new American Chevrolet ambulances, which is purpose built and completely different to anything we'd ever handled before with its powerful 6.2 litre engine. It looked very impressive, a real up market vehicle. I was on with Colin, an ambulance technician, who'd not worked on one before so we spent half an hour working out how to operate everything. We were the first crew out again and bang on the start of our twelve-hour shift the red 'phone went.

07:02 AM

OUR FIRST CALL was to a woman we've been transporting to hospital three times a week for longer than I've been at Central. She attends the Renal Dialysis Unit at the Royal Victoria Infirmary for sessions of kidney dialysis. She lives on the fourth floor of a tenement block and normally meets us at the entrance to the flats. Today she wasn't there. We climbed the stairs to her flat, rang the bell and after a while she let us in. She was in a bad way. She hadn't eaten for two

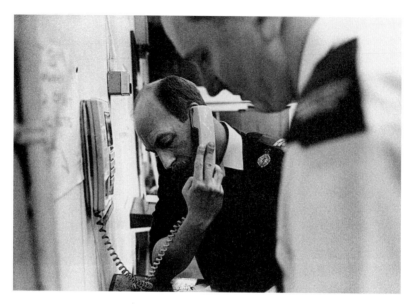

An emergency call on the hot line at Central.

days and felt lousy. There was nothing else for it, but to wrap her up nice and warm, pop her onto our carrying chair and gently take her down four flights of stairs to the ambulance. As we got her into the ambulance she was telling us how one side of her body had swollen up and she had little movement on the other. We radioed ahead to the hospital unit to warn them of her symptoms and when we arrived a doctor was waiting to examine her.

The regular dialysis patients we take in on the ambulance every week are people who couldn't really manage in a taxi. You get to know them over the years, and hear all about their families and what's happening in their lives. One of our regulars had some bad luck last week, she was burgled while she was at one of her sessions. She's now so unhappy and nervous that she's asked the council to move her to a different area. We had another old boy who's no longer with us, who always used to produce a bag of sweets, always the same sort of unwrapped toffees, and offer them to us. Sometimes he'd tell the attendant to take a couple for later. As the man grew older and weaker the crews had to start going into the house to pick him up. One day one of the lads went in with a carrying chair and saw that there was a pile of sweet wrappers on the table next to the old boy. As they were lifting him onto the chair he asked him why he'd suddenly changed to chocolate-covered toffees. 'That's all I've ever eaten,' he replied. Jack was bemused. 'But the ones you offer us aren't chocolate covered?'

'Oh no. That's because I only like the chocolate, not the toffees so I just suck the chocolate off.'

08:05 AM

THE CALL WAS to a RTA in St Andrew's Street, no further details. Driving up the street there was no sign of any accident. We'd been given the address of a hairdresser's shop, so pulled up and went in to find out if anyone had seen anything. Our patient was inside. Apparently she'd stepped out of the shop and been hit by a lad riding a mountain bike along the pavement. She'd been tossed up in the air, landed heavily and sustained a cut to her forehead. I checked her over and as a precaution put a cervical collar on her to support her neck and head. She had a bad laceration on the back of her head so we bandaged it up then took her to the hospital.

Some of the worst calls to road accidents start with a few sketchy details. We'd taken a patient from Hexham hospital down to Newcastle General and were on our way back along the A69, looking forward to getting that kettle on, when Control radioed us asking for our location. They then came back to say there were reports of a road accident on the A69, but they weren't yet sure of the exact position. We turned the blue lights on, and speeded along towards Hexham. It was one of those hunches based on local knowledge of a couple of blackspots which were ahead of us. Mind you, we'd have looked pretty stupid if we'd been going the wrong way.

Our guess had been right though and before long control came back with the exact location which was by then only a mile or so away. Traffic ahead was at a dead stop and there were no cars coming towards us – the usual indications that

Our bicycle victim.

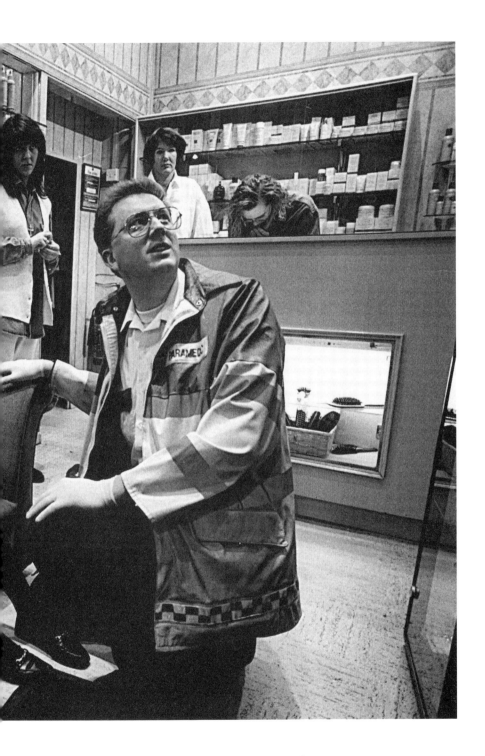

something was badly wrong. When we arrived at the end of the long line of traffic we were greeted with a scene of absolute devastation.

Normally, when cars collide they bounce off each other like snooker balls, but in this case the two cars had hit so squarely head on that they'd actually impacted together. We did the usual quick triage to assess how many were injured and who we should deal with first, but it was all a bit academic really. It wouldn't have taken too much paramedic training to tell that none of the occupants stood a chance. The two cars had been compressed in the space of a single vehicle. We managed to tell that there had been four people in one car and two in the other. The head injuries suffered by all but one passenger were so gruesome that there was only one patient even worth attempting to resuscitate, but even then we knew it wasn't a real possibility. When we realized that everyone had been killed I contacted Control and they sent out a doctor to certify death and call for an undertaker. The most useful thing we could do was help the firemen get the bodies out of the wreckage.

It was a cold March day and quite late in the afternoon, when the sun was low in the sky. It had been raining so the road was wet. Both cars were silver and had been belting along extremely fast in opposite directions. We could only assume that one car had overtaken a line of traffic on a sweeping bend and the driver coming the other way, facing into the sun, had been dazzled, and they'd collided. One of the policemen reckoned they must have hit at a combined speed of around 150 mph. Imagine running round a corner into a brick wall at that speed.

I got one of the bodies half way out of a car, but realized that he was trapped by his legs. The firefighters started to cut away the obstruction as I held him horizontally out of the way. Before long I wondered why my foot was feeling wet. When I looked down I could see that the massive head wound was pouring forth blood which was collecting in my shoe. But there was nothing I could do except hold on to the chap. It was a terrible sight, the worst accident I have ever seen. As we were dealing with that body I remember a fireman pushing at the tarpaulin under his feet asking what he was standing on. His colleague said, 'It's not *what* you are standing on, it's *who* you're standing on.' The person beneath had been so pulverized, every single bone was broken flat.

Major road accidents involve more variations of carnage than you can ever imagine, but the one constant thing is the smell. You can't get it out of your nostrils for ages afterwards. It's a strange sweet smell. I'm not sure how it arises, perhaps it's the hot oil on the engine or antifreeze on hot exhaust, or a combination of fuels that creates an aromatic cocktail. I don't know. I only know that after a road death I never remember the faces, only that sweet smell. Sometimes in a garage I'll feel uneasy for no obvious reason, and then realize that the smell is there as well.

After any major accident on a busy road you have to watch out for your own safety. There are two types of dangerous drivers: the ones who drive very slowly trying to get a good look at some mangled bodies and the others who are so fed up with being held up in a queue that they put their foot down as soon as they can, often just as they draw parallel with the very place you're trying to manoeuvre a stretcher.

Of course it's easy to become so engrossed in what you're doing that you can easily forget the dangers to yourself. Someone who must have been very late for his tea that day just managed to swerve and avoid me while I was working on releasing one of the victims. I couldn't believe it. If he'd been six inches closer there would have been more carnage at the incident. It's always said that our day-glo coloured jackets with the luminous stripes all over them are not easy to miss, a point he nearly proved!

After any grim accident we tend to go a bit quiet in the cab. You both know it has to sink in. Then as the day passes and you continue with other jobs, you begin to talk about it. Slowly at first, and if you sense your colleague doesn't want to talk, you respect that and change the subject. Each ambulance person has his or her own way of dealing with a traumatic experience. But I suppose that's the beauty of our job, we aren't given the time to dwell, you're always off on the next job. The controllers can't allow you to brood, there aren't enough ambulances to do that. They know you've got paperwork to fill in at the hospital, or you've got to clean up the ambulance, and an allowance is made for that. But it's never long before the radio bleeps and they ask you how soon it will be before you're clear. It is very much a case of the old conveyor belt, but there are times when it works to our advantage. It puts off the time when you have to deal with your grief. After all you can deal with that when you're on your own.

It's never the blood and gore that affects us, we see that every day. It's the small things which reveal the emotional side of any tragedy. The absolute waste. The shopping in the back of the car ready to cook for a family; the presents wrapped up ready for a celebration; the personal photographs that fall out when you're searching for some form of indentification.

One minute six people are having a good time and the next they're no longer with us. It is just so sad. Not only for them, but for their families. There are very good reasons for trying *not* to forget accidents like that. But when I'm in my own car and I've got the stereo going and the heater on, my family with me and I'm driving down the road, I'm like most others. It's easy to forget the reality of how fast you're going, or what your braking distances are. The last thing I'm thinking is that anything will happen to us.

It's frightening how often an accident involves someone taking their eyes off the road to fiddle with a switch or a radio. When people buy, or even steal, a car they seldom work out where the switches are or what you do with the array of knobs on the dashboard. We were called to a fatal accident the other day where someone had been killed because he hadn't learnt how everything worked before he drove off. He was just bowling along in his new car, left hand down fiddling with the radio. As he was trying to find the right station he took his eyes off the road, hit a curb, and turned over. He and his passenger were killed. A brand new car and he didn't even drive it home.

At another call a car had turned over because the driver was trying to get his rear window screen wiper going. He was pressing all the switches and looking in his rear view mirror to see if he'd activated it. He soon found himself upside down on the wrong side of the road sliding along on his roof, with traffic coming towards him. And foreign tourists who hire cars sometimes don't know their left from their right. Last summer we had a woman taking in the sights along Hadrian's Wall who was on the wrong side of the road! She was rewarded with a head-on collision. When we picked her up with her friend, neither of them could speak a word of English. One of the women was badly hurt, but my Norwegian is not too good. It was a case of smiling a lot along with plenty of physical reassurance and sign language. Mind you an irate Geordie is every bit as difficult to understand as a Norwegian!

10:00 AM

WHEN WE GOT back to Central we thought we'd fill the kettle just in case, for once, it wasn't connected to the 'phone. Lo and behold we had a rare success. We were just beginning to enjoy our tea in the duty room when the red 'phone went. I don't know who devised the sound of that klaxon-like warble, but it's mournfully penetrating and makes the calmest people jump.

10:15 AM

IT WAS A call to a head injury at a private girls' school on the other side of town. We weaved our way through the traffic which was quite heavy and were met at the school entrance by a teacher who showed us through to the medical room. The girl, who was being attended to by the matron, had suffered from headaches on a regular basis and that morning had woken up with a particularly bad one. She had got herself to school, but had slipped on the wet toilet floor

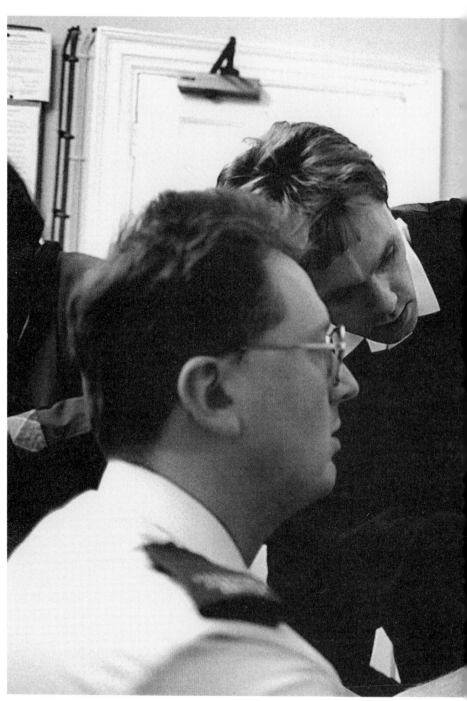

Fitting a cervical collar to the injured schoolgirl.

and banged her head on a sink. At the time she thought she would be all right, but two hours later she had complained of being unwell. That's when the school called us.

I checked to see how her eyes reacted. Both pupils constricted when the light shone on them, an indication that there was no serious head injury. Colin got as much of her medical history from the staff as possible. It's become an important part of our job, which can give the hospital a flying start in diagnosis and treatment. In this case the hospital would want to know if she fell, fainted, tripped or just came over giddy. They would also want to know about her past history of headaches and how they had been treated.

With a patient who has a head injury, but is conscious, we apply the Glasgow Coma Scale developed in Scotland. In the past everyone had a different idea as to how conscious someone was, the scale gives us well defined common parameters to which we can work. If, when asked, the patient knows their name, address and what day it is, and can touch their toes and open their eyes they score a maximum fourteen on the scale. But if their reply is something abstract or meaningless, they score lower. If they have absolutely no sign of life they score three. I don't know why it's three. Quite what you have to do to score zero is beyond me. The worst problem is when they don't know what day it is and ask me. I never know! This girl scored full marks.

We then wrapped her in a blanket, made her comfortable in the ambulance and, accompanied by one of the teachers, took her to the RVI. She was discharged later that day.

11:45 AM

WE WERE STILL at the RVI casualty when we were passed an emergency call to a collapse at Marlborough Crescent Bus Station with no further details. It's only five minutes away from the casualty so we were quickly on the scene. As we approached we were waved down frantically by an old teacher of mine. He'd been a Japanese prisoner of war and this had affected him mentally. As I braked alongside him he opened a plastic carrier bag and inside was a tortoise, it was totally surreal. I thanked him for showing it to us, said it was nice to see him again and was about to ask why he'd called us when he pointed dramatically further down the street to a small crowd.

On arrival a member of the crowd said, 'Quickly, he's round the back of the bus shelter,' but I could already see him. He was curled up in a ball, motionless and I could see his colour was not good. While I was checking him over I asked people what had happened. Did anyone see him collapse, had anyone done anything for him? One man said he had seen him clutch his chest and fall to the ground. Another had telephoned 999, but no one had cleared his airway or attempted any form of resuscitation. Someone else pointed to a pathetic looking dog, saying it belonged to the old man.

As always with a collapse, I had the first response case with me. This contains the most used piece of equipment on the ambulance, the bag and mask which enable us to breathe for a patient. This old boy's heart had stopped and so had his breathing. I carried out the full resuscitation protocol. The ambulance was parked next to the bus shelter so we swiftly moved the man onto our stretcher trolley and into the ambulance, resuscitating all the time.

As Colin jumped into the cab someone ran across with the man's dog. What can you do? Rather than waste time in discussion Colin put the dog in the passenger seat. Out of the corner of my eye as I wired his master up to the heart monitor I caught sight of the animal looking on. The screen showed that the man was in electrical mechanical disassociation (EMD), which means that electrical signals were telling the heart to fire, but the muscles were not responding therefore his heart had stopped pumping completely. The electrical signals can appear on the screen as though it's a normal heartbeat, but when you feel for a pulse there's nothing. The only treatment I could give was to inject the drug Adrenaline to attempt to get the heart firing again, and carried on with CPR. But there was still no response.

Colin radioed ahead to the RVI to ask them to stand by. We were on our way. Blue lights flashed, siren wailing, with

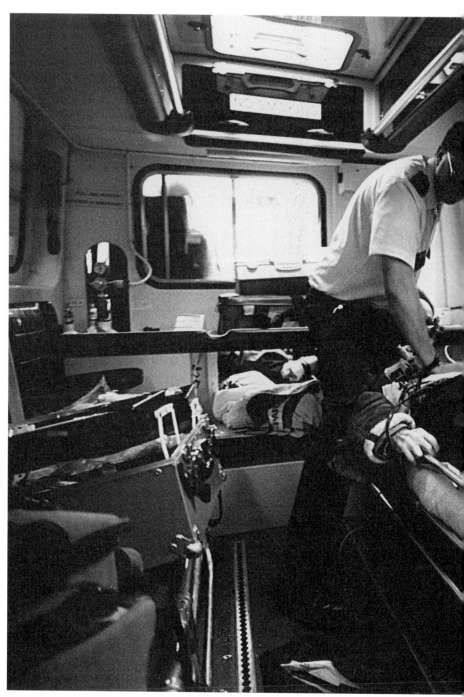

Resuscitation as we raced to the hospital.

Colin driving as smoothly as possible. However good the driver, it's no easy operation carrying out resuscitation in the back of an ambulance travelling at fifty or so miles an hour through the city centre. When we got to the hospital the staff were standing by and a doctor climbed on board to examine the patient. I carried on resuscitating as I explained the patient's history to him. The man was in his eighties, he'd had a past history of heart problems and he'd been unconscious for about twenty minutes before we arrived during which no one had been doing anything, which inevitably meant his brain had been starved of oxygen for at least that time.

The doctor checked the old chap over and said, 'Sorry lads, we're too late.' Time had caught up with him. We informed Control that this job was a Code Purple, the patient was dead, so they knew we'd be longer than usual at the hospital clearing up. Together with the nursing staff we went through all the old chap's pockets and collected his valuables: his watch, wallet, cards, etc. These were held for his next of kin. We then took him round to the mortuary and placed him on a slab.

It's physically and mentally exhausting resuscitating someone. But we can't sit back, put our feet up for a few minutes and have a cup of tea because we know the longer we're off the road, the more work we're putting onto our mates. You have to take a deep breath and tell yourself that the old boy had a good run.

It crosses your mind that if someone had immediately resuscitated him, it might have saved him. However, from our point of view, we'd done everything according to our protocol, everything in our power to give the old boy a fighting chance. Strange as it might sound the case was technically a success, even though the old boy died. We could both sleep well that night. The worst part of all was seeing his dog tied up outside the casualty department, obviously knowing something was wrong.

One of the saddest road accidents I was ever at happened some time ago, when a bloke was killed outright in a collision between his van and a car. When we arrived we saw the man slumped over the wheel, but being guarded by his dog. The dog was sitting in the corner panting and just looking at his master. I'm sure he knew what was going on. He looked so helpless, so lost. Because the car was really mangled up we had to get the dog out through the front window. Of course he couldn't tell me how he felt for his master, but his big, sad eyes said it all.

12:46 PM

WE RECEIVED THE call to the bus station at 11.45 a.m. The resus case took us an hour and one minute and we were straight into the next call – a RTA. Control said the accident had happened at the roundabout at Osborne Road. We went screaming off and arrived in about six minutes only to find there was nothing there. This is a problem, the adrenaline is flowing, you turn the corner, you expect to see all hell let loose, cars on their roofs and people screaming, but there's nothing there. Then you start to think to yourself is it a hoax, or are we in the wrong place, did I mishear the address?

We informed Control, but at the same time we drove around the immediate area to see if we could spot anything. After about five minutes Control radioed back to say it was Osborne Avenue, not Osborne Road. This happens often. If it's not road, its crescent or lane. Fortunately Osborne Avenue was only half a mile away. When we arrived there were two panda cars waiting. Colin pulled up and I jumped out. We soon realized it wasn't a serious road accident. A motorcycle had hit a car side on and thrown off the pillion passenger, who was a bit shaken up. I checked him over, put a collar on his neck and helped him into the ambulance. Once he was inside, I closed the doors and then started to get his leathers off which was a feat in itself. He looked like Giant Haystacks when he started, but by the time I'd peeled off five jumpers and six t-shirts and thermals, he was half

OVERLEAF: *Treating the injured motorcyclist.*

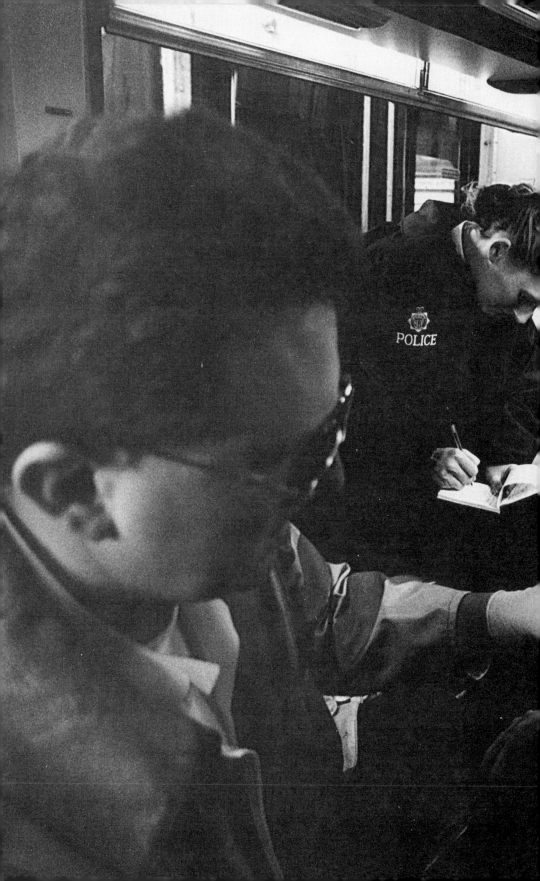

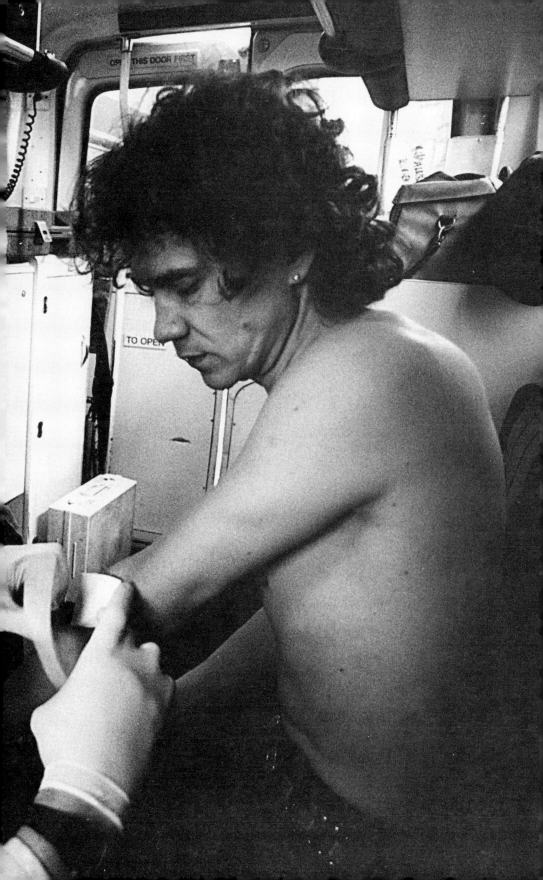

the man! I could see that he had bruised his ribs but otherwise he was all right. He would have been checked over at
the hospital and discharged.

Sometimes all your medical training goes out the window
and you get completely flummoxed. One of the lads at our
station, Andrew, was sent on a job which defied medical
knowledge. He was called to a road accident involving an old
boy who'd been walking slowly across the road when he was
hit by a car. When our lot turned up they found him in
what looked like a terrible way under the car. As they
walked across they saw that one leg appeared to have been
bent right behind his back, so that his foot was pointing
away from his back. The driver was in a state but said he
hadn't moved him, which of course was the right thing to do.

Andy was about to talk to him, quite expecting him to
be delirious with pain, when the man said, 'All right lads?' It
was them who should have been asking him that. Andy
looked and wondered if the old boy was in such deep shock
that he hadn't registered the pain from having his femur
folded backwards around his neck. Trying to play it down,
Andy said to the old boy that they had a bit of a problem
with his leg.

'Oh don't worry lads I'll get that sorted out.'

To their amazement he was more concerned about his
arm which he said had been grazed as he fell. He asked them
if they could just help him up and he could get on his way.
Andy started to think about the best approach to moving
the man without compounding the horrific injury, and what
he should do about pain relief. Suddenly as if he'd had
enough waiting round, the man started to move. Before
Andy could stop him the old boy shifted his weight over to
one side and offered his other hand for a lift up. As he did
the twisted leg fell with a thump to the road. Andy uttered
an exclamation which surprised the old boy. He knew he
could pick up his artificial leg later.

One of our lads arrived at another road accident to find
that neither the driver nor the passenger, a man and a
woman, were too badly hurt, but they were trapped inside.
The firefighters were happy because they could try out one

of their new toys, a pair of pincer-like cutters which hacked through car bodies like scissors cutting paper. The ambulance crew were dressing the facial cuts of the two patients and reassuring them that they were going to be all right when the man saw the firefighters approaching with cutters in hand, sizing up the car. He suddenly became very panicky as he realized that they were going to cut the roof off so that they could get the couple out. They stopped and explained that the way the car had buckled there were no options. He pleaded with them to have another look, convinced that the damage was not that bad. Couldn't the fire brigade perhaps get them out through the window? From outside it was quite clear that drastic measures would have to be taken, but he still asked them not to do too much damage. He was getting very agitated, so the paramedic asked the firefighters to hold back while he calmed the driver down. As ever in these situations the truth eventually emerges. He said that he hoped there wouldn't be too much damage because it was his wife's brand new car, and the woman beside him was not his wife. On top of which he'd told his missus that he was away on business in Scotland. The paramedic eventually convinced him that there was no alternative but to cut the roof off, which the fire brigade did with great relish. We were all wondering how he explained to his wife that she now had a convertible.

Some years back one of the crews at Central got a call to a road accident where a bus had hit a pedestrian and driven right over her. The victim was lying underneath the bus when the ambulance turned up. The first action was to find out what injuries the patient had sustained. Bryan crawled underneath and found that the person was conscious, but had received a broken leg. He crawled back out and told his colleague what equipment he needed to move the patient, then crawled back under to help her. His colleague tapped him on his legs which were sticking out from the bus, to ask if he wanted analgesic gas, which he shouted out that he did. While he was talking away to the patient he heard the sirens of the fire brigade arriving. He thought nothing much about it except that his colleague would tell them they were not needed and carried on talking to the patient. The next thing he knew, his legs were being grabbed and he was dragged out from under the bus. When he looked up he discovered a pleased looking fireman, who was not so happy when he saw the paramedic jacket. The lad who did it was probably a rookie and, like anyone who has just finished their training, eager to increase experience by removing the victim. The training has been amended since then!

Last summer we were called out to an accident on the A1 involving two cars that had struck each other at high speed. Two ambulances were sent in convoy. When we arrived the cars were about two hundred yards apart. The first crew went to look after the car with two occupants, while we dealt with the other car which just had a driver. As we approached we could see that the wing, the driver's door and the rear door were all off. In fact there wasn't anything left of the driver's side, it had been sliced off. Miraculously, however, the driver had not been touched, it had been such a clean demolition job. It had taken us ten minutes to get there, but the driver was still sitting, staring straight ahead, absolutely rigid. His hands were gripping the steering wheel, his knuckles white with the pressure he was exerting. I've never seen anything like it. He was locked solid with fear. I can only think that at the moment he'd realized the car coming towards him at about 70 mph was going to hit him, he'd had a vision of imminent death. Now he sat there in a state of disbelief that he was alive. He was in total shock.

As I checked him over I felt like saying that he'd been unbelievably lucky, but thought the truth might send him into even worse shock. So even though I was kneeling beside a man who was sitting in a car with no side, I tried to act as though this was something we saw all the time and reassured him that he was all right. Slowly the grip on the wheel eased, he became less rigid and he stopped staring ahead maniacally. It was as if he'd come back to life and the adrenaline had begun to flow again. He then began to cry uncontrollably. He just sobbed and sobbed. Every emotion mixed up, anger, fear and relief. I'd already put a collar around his neck so we lifted him out onto the trolley, and took him into the ambulance. On the way to hospital he began to relax even more and kept reliving those few moments, talking about how lucky he was, how by the grace of God he'd come through. By the time we got him to hospital he was a born again Christian!

We found out later that the driver of the other car was drunk. After the crash he'd realized he was in trouble, so he'd agreed with his passenger, who was sober, that they would switch seats. There were no witnesses, apart from our patient who was in no state to make any sense.

The police took statements from the lads who thought they'd got away with it until, that is, they arrived at hospital and were examined. The police had their suspicions and spoke to the staff who confirmed that the inebriated man had in fact been driving. Both lads had been wearing seat belts and had been bruised by the impact. The bruising showed that they could only have been sitting the opposite way to the statements they'd given the police. The passenger had a bruise on his left shoulder and the driver on his right.

So they both ended up being charged.

13:30 PM

THE NEXT CALL was a doctor's urgent case to pick up a lady from an old people's home and take her into hospital for tests.

We see all sorts of living conditions in old people's homes, from places you wouldn't want to send an animal, to some like this one which was really well run. You can tell as soon as you go through the door how good they are; by the decor, the attitude of the staff and the looks on the residents' faces. In the worst places they're all left sitting in isolated chairs around a soulless room, with nothing to stimulate or promote any feelings of well being. As we walked into the lounge this morning the old people were having a sing song so we joined in while the staff organized the patient.

The little old lady that we had come for was also singing, but you could tell she wasn't too well. She'd had stomach bleeding for the last four days. The matron offered us a cup of tea and a slice of fruit cake but, tempting as they were, we declined. We took our patient up to one of the wards at Newcastle General Hospital. It was a technically undemanding job, but very satisfying.

15:52 PM

WE REALIZED THAT we had not had our meal break. We shot back to the station, but again the telephone was in love with the kettle and refused to be parted. I began to wish I'd taken the matron's cake!

15:55 PM

THE CALL WAS to a collapse at a pub in Spittletongues, which is near the RVI, about a five-minute race away.

I have to say that for me, the perfect place to die would be a pub. However, when the call is to a pub at around chucking out time, you can be fairly sure the patient will be suffering from a little more than having imbibed the usual three pints. Not so long ago though we had a call to a pub in the city centre which was an exception to this general theory.

We went straight to the location without even having to refer to a map, and when we arrived we knew just which door to head for. As we walked in the landlord came across to meet us and pointed through the mass of people to a place near the bar. Through the haze and smoke we could just about make out an old chap sitting very still in amongst about ten or fifteen other old lads who were talking away and gently swaying.

The worst thing about being called to a pub, apart from the obvious torture of not being able to have a pint yourself, is that the customers won't move out of the way when they see you. They think you're just another punter pushing your way to the bar. Even when you shout, 'Excuse me, excuse me, can I get past?' they look, but there's no way they're going to let you through. The landlord has dialled 999, but he hasn't told the clientele that an ambulance is coming. I'm sure that several times I've been mistaken for a stripogram, which doesn't bear thinking about – it wouldn't be a pretty sight. Whatever they may think, the one thing they don't think is that you're a paramedic on call.

Pushing our way through the crowd across to the group by the bar, we could see that they'd all been there for some time enjoying the ale. A couple of them turned their attention to us. They greeted us with a cheery 'Hello lads!' as if we'd come to join the party. It was obvious who our patient was and he didn't look too well. He certainly wasn't swaying like his friends. His face was purple and he'd probably been dead for several rounds. But there he was sitting bolt upright, still wearing a smile and a flat cap. It was obvious that his mates were oblivious to the exact state of his health, and had been propping him up while trying to coax him into having another pint. As we started to examine him all we got from his mates was 'He'll be OK. He's often like this'. They were absolutely gone themselves and they thought *he* was just legless as well. More to the point, they'd just bought him a pint and were starting to worry that he wasn't going to buy his round. They were right to worry on that score anyway.

We pushed the table out of the way ignoring the 'Mind my drink, son!' and got him onto the floor and the old lads just didn't know what was going on. Of course, while we were resuscitating the music was still belting out from the jukebox – it never goes off in these situations, you just have to hope you're resuscitating to the right tempo. We knew the man was well dead, but I was just going through the delicate art of intubating him to maintain his airway and get air down into his lungs when I got a tap on my shoulder and there was one of his mates saying to me 'Would you like a pint or a whisky or something?' And another added 'One for the road?' They were being kind, of course, but they didn't seem to realize what was going on. There wasn't much we could do for the old boy, but I can think of worse places and ways to die. Judging by the smile on his face he'd been happy to go with a pint in his hand as well.

At the collapse this afternoon we found a chap leaning against the wall of the pub, looking very grey and his fingers were 'cyanosed', very blue, through lack of oxygen. He was breathing shallowly and with pain. I spoke to him, reassured him that he'd be all right, then asked his name and what his medical history was as we lifted him onto our chair and into the ambulance. He'd had a heart attack before and suffered from angina. In the case of angina the blood vessels that surround the heart have narrowed. When a person over exerts themselves the heart tries to absorb more oxygen to cope with the extra work load, but the blood vessels of an angina sufferer aren't wide enough to allow a greater flow of blood, therefore the heart comes under undue strain and they feel pain. Most people who suffer from angina are on nitrates. These can be given as tablets or by spray. In the ambulance we carry Buccal-nitrate tablets. These dilate the vessels round the heart, so more blood can flow and relieve the pain. In this man's case I put him on the monitor and gave him oxygen. As we were so close to the hospital and he seemed to be improving every minute, I didn't give him any tablets.

He was a cheery old chap. Once we were underway and he'd been breathing oxygen for a few minutes, I asked him how he was feeling and he said, 'Oh, much better now. But son, I must have been bad. I was on my way home and my bags were getting heavier and heavier. I got as far as the pub and thought I'd go in, have a pint and a sit down. But I didn't feel any better so I left to call you. I tell you, in forty years that's the first time I've ever left a pint, so I knew I was bad.' Then he added with a smile, 'Mind you there's a good pint in there if you want to go back and get it!'

As ambulance men we take our jobs very seriously and are keen to make sure that the public gets the best care we can give them. As part of our continuing training we like to make sure that we know how to get in and out of all the drinking establishments in the city, and that we know our

OPPOSITE: *The patient collected from outside a pub.*

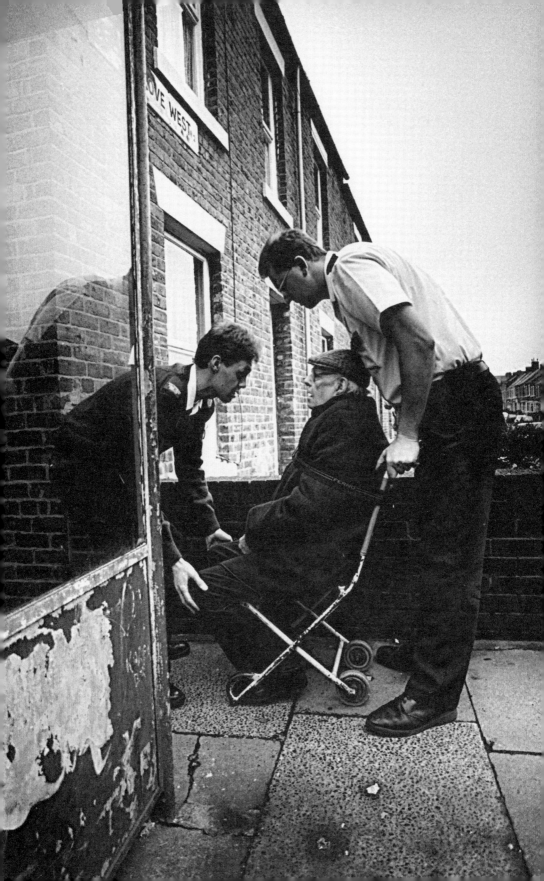

way around each of them instinctively. To keep ourselves up to date, we selflessly give up much of our own time to research the layouts of all the bars in Newcastle. While we're there we take the research one stage further by observing the effects of alcohol on the adult human being. Not only do we give up our own time and money to do this, but we also offer ourselves as guinea pigs for the observations. On many Thursday, Friday or Saturday nights you can find us heading for Newcastle's Bigg Market along with all the hundreds of others. It's *the* place to go, the Mecca of the North, coachloads come from all over the region. The Bigg Market is really an area of streets in the city centre, with a pub on every corner and loads in between. It's a fantastic place. It's not unusual to walk down the Bigg market and find a naked person standing on a street corner, some poor lad on his stag night who's been stripped off by his mates and abandoned.

If you haven't experienced the place at first hand it's difficult to imagine. You've sometimes got to join a queue twenty yards long to get into a pub, there'll be that many people desperate to get in. As one person leaves the crowd control officers – bouncers to you and me – let in another. Once you're in you find out where the toilets are, look for the bar and off you go. It's out with the paper money, wave it around and eye up your barman until, eventually, you get served. The music is so loud you can't hear yourself think. You can forget everything.

There's always a load of girls with white high heels, short skirts and skimpy tops dancing around their handbags. They've got all their warpaint on and they're looking for a bit of action. It's all good stuff. You have to see it to believe it. The beer warms up very quickly, it's got no head on it, flat as can be, but it tastes better with every pint. You can't move for the pressure of people and there's no way you can be heard above the music. When you're a punter with a few drinks inside It's great fun.

When you're a stone cold sober paramedic on duty things are different.

Normally during the week it takes about five minutes to make the journey from the ambulance station via the Bigg

Market to the hospital. But if you get calls on a weekend night that same journey can take twenty minutes, because there are so many people walking across the road in front of you, screaming and shouting. Early in the evening it's all good humoured; the later it gets the more like a madhouse it becomes. People are falling down everywhere or vomiting over their mates. You can guarantee that if you're on a weekend late shift you'll be down there before the night's out. The majority of the calls come in as collapses in the street. When you get to the collapse it's always the same story. They've spent all their money, at least thirty pounds, on drink, fallen down drunk, banged their head, their new clothes are ripped, their jacket's off, they've lost all their valuables, including their watch, and their keys. But ask them how much they've had to drink and it's always 'two or three pints maximum'. Anybody who admits to having had more than three must be a complete alcoholic. We always multiply their amount by three and add another four for good measure. A drunk never tells you how much they've actually had.

Of course they've usually been in a fight. We get there, open the back doors and half a dozen of them pile in. So you say, 'Hold on lads, who's the patient?'

They point to a lad who looks in a bit of a worse state than the rest. 'It's him.'

'What's happened?'

'He's been filled in and he's unconscious.'

Even though you can always tell that his real problem is that he's drunk, I never query their diagnosis, it would cause too many problems. By now they're arguing who's going for a ride with him and you know that they're not going to be pleased if you contradict them. In any case, even if he is just drunk, we still have to take him. If we left someone on the street drunk and later they stepped in front of a car and got killed it would be on our conscience. So the easiest thing to do is take him and his willing mates round to hospital.

Sometimes there's been a fight and the two people involved have done some damage to each other, usually by punching and kicking each other around the face. Many times the mates of one of the lads have come along and laid into the other bloke, then his mates hear about this and have a go at the first lot. By the time we get there, they're often still laying the odd punch, but mainly it's verbal abuse. We push them onto the ambulance and whisk them off. But then in the ambulance we've got the original two patients who don't like each other, and also their mates who are too drunk to realize where they are and start fighting all over again. So I'm in the back calming them down: 'Look lads, I don't mind a bit of agro in the back of the ambulance, but let's try and keep it calm when you get to hospital because there are sick people there. I mean you wouldn't like it if it was your mother.' It usually works as soon as you relate it to how they'd like their mother or granny treated and these big beefy lads calm down.

Equally, I've seen people who've had a fight in which they've kicked hell out of each other, but after we've calmed them down they realize they've just been silly boys. By the time we get to the hospital they're shaking hands, even hugging each other. I'm in the middle like the big matchmaker saying, 'Please invite me to the wedding.'

Then you get the calls to people who are still inside the packed pub or club. It's not so bad if they're near the door, but if they're a long way inside then it's time for the familiar ambulance man's cry, 'Bring out your dead'. As soon as you arrive you know it's going to be a waste of time trying to get in, it's chock-a-block. So you stand at the door and shout to anyone who'll listen, 'What's happened?' and you'll get, 'He's drunk,' or 'He's fallen down,' or, 'He's had a fight,' or all three. Then comes the second part of the ambulance cry, 'Can he walk?' You get as much information as you can and usually his mates will have already started to fight their way out with him. We had one patient who was brought to us by being passed over the crowd's heads to the door.

It's not only blokes who get involved in fights. In fact I think the most ferocious fighters are the girls. They can be vicious with their nails out. There is nothing I used to like better, when I was younger, than watching girls fighting. A favoured method of attack is to pull your opponent's hair out. We often turn up to find a half bald girl, crying, make up all over her face, nails missing and of course one heel off. That's the classic, one heel on, one off, so as you pull up they clomp towards you.

Of course sometimes a report from a pub of a collapse turns out to be serious. One we went out to recently seemed like any other call we'd had that night in and around the Bigg Market. We got it as a collapse with no more information, except the address, which was one of the busiest streets in Newcastle. We kept on bowling along there and eventually got flagged down by a group of drunk, but concerned lads standing under a pedestrian bridge. Our casualty was in the middle of the group, lying on the pavement very still. There were no lights under the bridge and it was very dark. As we got down to examine him they told us that a few of them had climbed up onto the metalwork under the bridge, and had been swinging around having a good laugh when this lad had fallen, banging his head. He was lying on his back, and his mates were all well out of their heads, shouting and shaking him. I checked him over and he wasn't breathing, nor could I find a pulse. I was going to have to carry out a full resusciation. My mate ran to the ambulance to get the paramedic drugs case and the heart monitor and I started CPR. That was bad enough outside with so little light, but as if that wasn't enough as soon as I started work two of his mates grabbed hold of him again. One had his leg and the other was over the top of him. I had to push them off, but as soon as I pulled one away, the second would get on top of him again screaming at him, 'Come on, come on, don't die.' They knew their mate was poorly and wanted the best for him, but they were so drunk that they just wanted to get him home and turn the clock back. They'd probably seen people being resuscitated on TV and knew that when a paramedic starts pumping the chest and trying to get a tube down the throat, things aren't good. A few minutes earlier they'd all been having a good laugh as they climbed up on the bridge. Now they were losing their mate. They hadn't come out that night to see him die. I knew their reactions would only get worse when they saw the paddles from the

Off we go again.

defibrillator appear. Thank God a policeman arrived in a panda car. I remember looking up and seeing him spread his arms, flapping them up and down and herding the lads into a corner like geese or sheep. He was saying very firmly, 'If you'se go near him, I'm going to lock you up, I'll have you.' He saved the day because we couldn't have managed to resuscitate the patient and keep his mates off on our own. One lad went absolutely berserk, what with the drink and the shock of what had happened, it was all too much for him. There's no question about it, they would have started on us. More police arrived to control the group. We did all we could but unfortunately he didn't make it. We were knackered by the end of that one, really drained.

16:14 PM

WE CLEARED FROM our angina sufferer and were sent straight to an emergency call in the north of Newcastle. A 999 call had come from a doctor who'd been to an old people's sheltered accommodation home, where he'd examined the patient and found she had pneumonia. There are a number of old people's homes springing up in Newcastle but I'd never heard of this particular one before. We were only given the name of the building and the general area. Once we found it the hardest part was getting into the place. Most old people's sheltered accommodation has remote security locks on the main door but I don't think anyone bothers to show the old people how to use them. At night we always have particular difficulty in getting into these places. Fortunately this afternoon somebody was going in to visit and they got their relative to open the door.

When we got inside we faced a very sad situation. The woman was terribly frail. We wrapped her little body in a blanket and put her on our chair. Her husband was with her, a big, stout man, crying his eyes out. I said to him, 'Don't worry, we'll look after her, we'll make sure she's OK.' But I was fairly certain she was never going to return. We took our time, made her comfortable then wheeled her over to him and he gave her a final kiss, it was really heart rending. In the ambulance we gave her plenty of tender loving care, some oxygen and a smooth ride to the hospital.

16:34 PM

WE WERE TOLD to drive to a point on one of the main roads leading out towards Hexham to act as A & E cover. At times in Control it's like a chess game. The station which normally covers that area was out on a long involved emergency call, as was the next station, so we were pulled out of central Newcastle to cover quite a large rural area. I used to work out in Hexham so know the area, which can be more confusing than the city streets.

Some years ago when I was working at one of our rural stations we got an emergency call to say that an elderly lady had collapsed at a farm way out in the wilds of Wanney. The only other address detail we were given was the name, Sheep Farm. The man who was calling had put the 'phone down, often a sign of someone in a panic. We had some idea of the general direction and as we set off I opened up our ordnance survey map which seemed to grow larger than the cab. My mate drove along, pushing the map out of her face as I unfolded it. The only place bearing any resemblance to the name was a Sheep Valley, so we aimed for it and hoped. We got to the area and struck lucky. There on a gate was the name Sheep Farm, but no road, not even a track leading anywhere from it, just a field sloping down into what the map had told us was Sheep Valley. There was nobody around to ask, and of course we were having radio problems, and therefore out of communication with Control.

In the distance, somewhere down in the valley we saw smoke, so decided to aim for that. A few yards further along the road was a cart track which vaguely headed towards the smoke so we took it. We decided to switch off the blue lights since our speed was unlikely to be any danger to the grazing cattle.

Down we went, opening and shutting one gate after another as we crossed the fields before we found the source of the smoke, an old ramshackle, but picturesque cottage, with a small wooden sign saying, 'Sheep Farm'. With the ambulance engine switched off there were no sounds except those of the countryside. The front door was open so we called out but there was no reply. Fearing the worst we went inside. There were signs of recent habitation down in the old fashioned kitchen, cups and saucers in the sink, the fire not long since stoked up. We went up the stairs into all the bedrooms, and there too it was easy to tell that someone had been there not long before. It was like a land-locked *Marie Celeste*. Very eerie.

It had taken us nearly forty minutes to get to the farm, but it seemed it was all for nothing. What made matters worse was the fact that we were still out of radio communication and there was no telephone for us to contact base. We had one more look around to be absolutely sure no one was lying behind the back door or in any other less obvious corner, and decided we had no choice but to return to the road and try to contact base. This was obviously the place and, as ever in these situations, you worry that someone who needs your help is not getting it. We made our way back up to the main road, the revving ambulance bumping its way across the field disturbing the peace of the countryside and making our presence very obvious. As we turned out onto the main road an old chap in a Landrover pulled up ahead of us. I thought we were going to get a rocket for trespassing on his land, but all we got was, 'Have you come for Mrs Smith?' We told him we had. 'Well follow me. She's at my place, just down there.' On the way along the road we discussed the possibility that the old lady was obviously in a bad state and had been taken in by her neighbour. In the second farmhouse we asked the lady sitting at the table eating a biscuit and holding a cup of tea where we'd find Mrs Smith. Slightly puzzled she said that it was her. She was obviously not too ill because she offered us a cup before we set off. After our exertions it was tempting, but we declined. As we were gathering up her bits and pieces the farmer told us that he'd heard the old lady, who lived on her own, was a bit weak after a bout of 'flu and he had taken her to his place while he summoned help. Sometimes the obvious doesn't connect at first. Then we realized that the lack of a telephone down at Sheep Farm meant that she couldn't have called us herself. When her neighbour had 'phoned and spoken to Control and they'd asked the lady's name, he'd said 'It was Mrs Smith of Sheep Valley Farm. He hadn't said she was *at* her farm, there was no need. He could see she was sitting there quite happily in front of him. I'm sure the telephone that sat in the corner was a new fangled object to him and was only used for special occasions, such as calling for the police, fire or ambulance. He certainly wasn't going to waste their time or his money with unnecessary chat.

17:43 PM

AFTER JUST OVER an hour sitting waiting in the ambulance we were told to attend an accident. It was still rush hour and kerb-to-kerb cars so we had to weave in and out of the traffic. Each set of lights we came to turned red. Obviously we can cross red lights but we have to treat them as give way junctions, so we wound up the wailing siren and crept across until we were sure the cars with right of way were going to stop. It never ceases to amaze me how many drivers still try to race across ahead of us. They may well have plenty of time and room, but it has the effect of slowing us down because we're never sure whether the car behind will have seen us. If only people would stop straight away so that we knew they'd seen us.

People's reactions to seeing an ambulance on an emergency are very different, sometimes unexpected in timing, but never surprising in execution. As we moved along most drivers saw us in their rear view mirrors and pulled over. Everyone, except a red Ford Escort – there's always one! You don't know what's going through their mind, you only know they won't pull over. They're not the only nuisance. Occasionally we'll look in the mirror and see a car right up tight behind us. What he wants to do is take advantage of the clear road left behind us. They annoy us intensely. It's extremely dangerous and totally illegal. At the other extreme

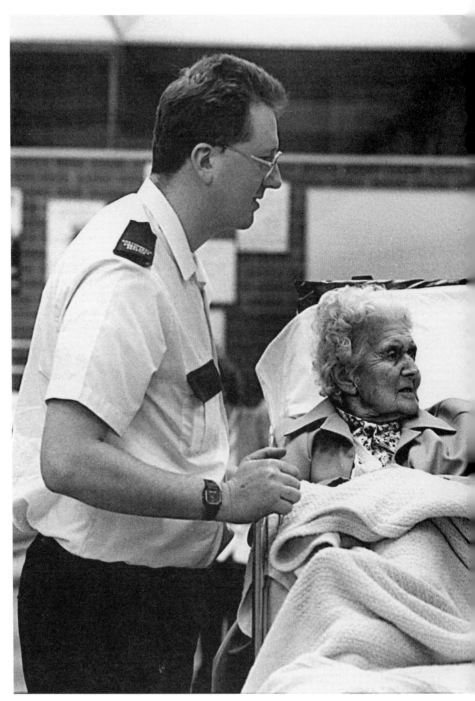

Handing a patient over in the RVI's casualty department.

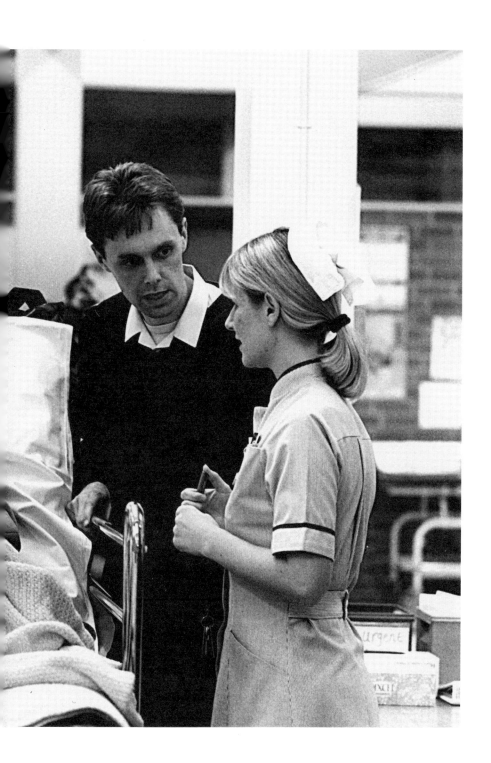

some drivers go to great lengths to get out of our way. I've seen them mount curbs, wheel trims flying off, in their eagerness to clear our path. Every time we pass a queue of traffic on one of the bridges across the Tyne I wonder if one of these over eager drivers will go too far and end up in the river. Then there are the drivers who freeze when they suddenly realize that the loud wailing noise they can hear is coming from the big ambulance with flashing lights which is fast approaching from behind and they'll stop dead. Usually this is on a corner or right alongside a traffic island, effectively blocking the road to us and forcing us into some strange manoeuvres. It's much better if they pull up further down the road. On a dual carriageway or a motorway, we try to go up the centre of the stationary traffic. It's like the parting of the Red Sea as cars move to either side. There's always one rogue car, however, which decides to cross from one lane to the other thinking they're helping us.

Despite the best efforts of a good many drivers to slow us down we got to this lad's house within eight minutes and saw the parents looking out of the window. As we jumped out dad was locking the front door and mum was walking up the path with the boy. He'd been playing on some nearby roadworks and fallen awkwardly. I could see the clothes he was wearing were pretty old and were caked in mud so I asked his mother if I could cut off his sleeve, to see how bad the injury was. She agreed. I talked to the lad while I was doing this to get his confidence. After I'd cut it away all I could see was deep bruising. We don't carry x-ray equipment on the ambulance, but from the way he was holding his arm, it certainly looked broken. Children don't want someone tying a sling round them unless it is really necessary, so I got him to support his bad arm with his good one. He was a plucky lad and seemed unconcerned about his injury. We had a relatively smooth journey to the Newcastle General, although anyone following us would have thought we were drunk as we kept swerving to avoid the potholes. I got his parents to book him in at the reception desk in casualty, while I took him to the triage desk for a nurse to assess how quickly he needed to be seen by a doctor.

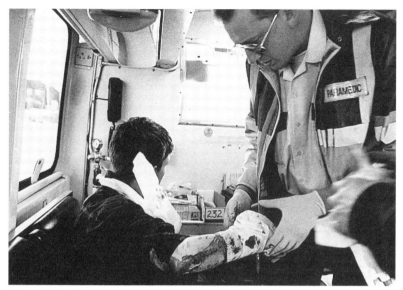

Boys will be boys.

Nothing that children get up to surprises me. I remember we had a call to say a boy had fallen out of a train. When we got to the area there was some confusion about where the lad had fallen and where we should park. The police were also looking for him. We were beginning to think it was a hoax call until we came across this kid who told us that his friend hadn't fallen from a train, he had fallen from a tree by a railway line. The two lads had been caught pinching apples and had been chased by the owner along the banks of the Tyne. In an effort to dodge him they'd decided to get up onto the railway track. A high wall stood in the way, but his mate had seen a tree alongside it and thought the best way over was to climb that and scramble along one of the branches which hung across the wall. He had managed to climb the tree all right but had slipped off the branch and fallen twenty feet.

As we were talking to the boy we were joined by a doctor who'd been called out and a man from one of the houses. The doctor questioned the boy who reckoned that his friend had hurt his back badly and was about a mile away. I made the decision to carry the scoop stretcher, my basic resuscitation equipment and some analgesic pain relief in the form of Entonox gas. It was hard going since it was getting dark as we set out along the river bank in single file and we were ankle deep in mud. And, added to that, our torches were running low. Unfortunately my mate brushed past a small branch of a fir tree which flicked back, caught the doctor in the face and dislodged her contact lenses. We now had a doctor with blurred vision in an already difficult light! It was too far to waste time returning so we guided her onwards.

After what seemed forever we found the boy lying on his back between the tree and the embankment wall. He was conscious and talking. As a precaution I put a cervical collar around his neck but when I examined him I found he had complete movement. He had been severely winded but was more shocked than injured. I checked him over and relayed what I was doing to the doctor who couldn't see a thing. We put the lad on the stretcher and strapped him down. But then we had to get him back. Unfortunately we had no portable radio communication to ask for back up assistance. We debated whether to return to the ambulance and radio for help, but thought that it would take too long. In the end each of us took a corner of the stretcher, while the boy's friend guided the doctor. The ground was difficult and the boy was quite a weight, so throughout the journey we kept stopping to change our position. We'd been all right getting there in single file, but it was a damned sight more difficult with two of us each side of the stretcher. I remember my mate fell badly, but he kept going.

At last we reached the ambulance and as soon as we got the lad inside I sat down. I was knackered. At the hospital I thanked the doctor for her help, then the police took her home because she couldn't see to drive. My mate was given an injection for his bad back and was off sick for days. The only person who seemed to enjoy it all was the patient.

DESPITE BEING THREE quarters of an hour away

from the end of our shift we were told to return to the station for our half-hour meal break. We looked at each other and said words to the effect of some hope!

18:20 AM

THE RED 'PHONE rang. It was a local job, barely three minutes' drive, to a collapse at a bus stop. When we arrived at what we hoped would be tonight's quick and simple last case, a concerned man was at the bus stop waving us down and pointing to a man on the ground. As we pulled up I looked out of the window and saw that it was one of our regulars. He was giving an Oscar-winning performance, shaking, shamming unconsciousness, it was the best simulated fit I'd seen for weeks. The man who had waved us down grabbed me as soon as I got out of the cab. He was deeply concerned, which showed in his voice, 'Come on, quickly, he's in a bad way, I've never seen anything like this before.'

I knelt down and said, 'Hello Mike, it's the ambulance here, are you going to come with us?' But true to his actor's calling there was no reaction, he just kept fitting. So I said again, 'Mike, it's the ambulance here, are you going to come with us now?' At that, he stopped fitting, promptly stood up and was on his feet before I was. You could almost hear the applause for the paramedic, the miracle worker. We could hear people saying, 'Did you see that? All he did was speak to him!'

When we got to the hospital I felt somewhat guilty about taking him in to casualty. You could see the look on some of the staff's faces saying 'Oh no, not him again'. He was told to sit down but I bet three minutes after we'd left he was on his way out again. Still, what a wonderful way to end the week, performing a miracle in the middle of Newcastle!

OVERLEAF: *Receiving another emergency call.*